Wool as an Apparel Fiber

Wool

as an Apparel Fiber

by Giles E. Hopkins

Rinehart & Company, Inc.
New York Toronto

Printed in the United States of America

Library of Congress Catalog Card Number: 53–9194

To Mr. F. Eugene Ackerman

His encouragement, advice and considerable prodding made this work possible.

ACKNOWLEDGMENT is made to F. Eugene Ackerman, President of The Wool Bureau, Inc., New York, and the Department of Science and Technology of the International Wool Secretariat, London, for their advice, criticism and suggestions; and to Beulah Adkins for her painstaking care in typing and proofing the manuscript and her encouragement as it passed through its many stages of development.

G. E. H.

Preface

Probably no fiber used by the textile industry is more complicated in its structure than wool. Perhaps no other fiber has been so little understood for so long a history of use in yarn and fabric. The industry has had to wait for many generations to learn some of the secrets of its composition and behavior; the revelation of which has only recently become possible by the use of such scientific developments as the electron microscope, servo-operated testers capable of taking into account time-temperature-load-deformation relationships, and x-ray diffraction units. The resulting data are highly technical and sometimes as complex as is the fiber they describe.

"WOOL AS AN APPAREL FIBER" with Giles E. Hopkins as author is intended to popularize these scientific findings and to sketch briefly the fascinating technical background of wool production, manufacture and use. The transformation of the protective coats of millions of sheep to form protective garments for millions of people has created an industry of first importance. The versatility of wool has satisfied the needs of the consumer and continues to do so. Widespread dissemination of the kind of information presented here is a service to the industry and to the people which it serves. The author is to be commended for providing it in such compact and interesting form and with so much technical accuracy. Understanding of the reasons for outstanding performance makes for greater appreciation on the part of the user of the heritage of wool and of its promise for the future.

EDWARD R. SCHWARZ

Professor of Textile Technology
Head, Textile Division
Massachusetts Institute of Technology

Contents

Introduction

The story of wool reaches back before the time of written records and is closely interwoven with man's slow advance into modern civilization. The sheep has figured prominently in religious traditions and symbolisms, and through the ages the laws of great nations have included powerful measures for the protection of sheep and wool commerce, so important to national wealth. From the 16th Century onward it has been decreed that all judges must sit upon a woolsack and all must swear fealty to the king by kneeling upon wool so that they might never forget that wool was the basis of England's greatness. As late as 1792, England prohibited the exportation of textile machinery. The first woolen card reached the United States in two separate parts which arrived in different shipments. They were identified as agricultural machinery.

Within the last six years, the United States has become the world's largest consumer of wool and the most important producer of textiles, both in terms of yardage and

"From the 16th Century onward it has been decreed that all judges must sit upon a woolsack and all must swear fealty to the king by kneeling upon wool . . ."

dollar value. It has captured this proud position from the United Kingdom which held it for four centuries.

The American wool textile industry has the largest production capacity for its kind in the world. It comprises 829 establishments engaged in some or all of the processes of converting greasy wool into finished fabrics. It employed in 1950 an average of 140,000 persons and paid out wages in excess of $400 million. It turned out products valued at over $2 billion, including woolen and worsted fabrics valued at almost $1½ billion.

The conversion of wool textiles into men's, women's, and children's clothing engages the major portion of the highly paid labor of 350,000 men and women in the tailored clothing industry. The finished products made of wool textiles, including clothing, blankets and upholstery, had a total retail value in 1950 of $6 to $6½ billion.

During the past two years the manufacturer and the public have been exposed to a barrage of propaganda aimed at selling the initial production of a host of new fibers. Some claims went so far as to state that new fibers had been created which in themselves combined all of the desirable qualities of wool. This type of claim is now disappearing and in its place we find performance claims focused on individual characteristics.

The presentation of each new fiber is accompanied by predictions of huge losses in wool demand. This enthusiastic adventure in the crystal-gazing functions of market research is obviously misleading when it is recalled that population growth and improvements in living standards will mean tremendous expansion in fiber consumption with little possibility of any extensive increase in wool production. It is imperative that additional fibers shall be provided to meet this demand, and wool must continue in those uses where its peculiar properties are most vital, while new fabrics are created from wool in combination with other fibers to compensate for their inherent weaknesses.

The acceptance of wool as the ideal fiber in many types of apparel has become so much a part of our thinking that we seldom stop to consider why wool has gained such an important place in our daily lives. Indeed the very versatility of the fiber may confuse us in our attempts to define just why wool is so valuable in each of its widely varied uses—and to ignore the difficulties which are encountered when the complete pattern of wool properties is not available. Wool produces a wide range of textures, from diaphanous crepes for evening dresses weighing 3-4 ounces per 56-inch-wide yard to luxurious fleeces and heavy melton overcoatings weighing 28-36 ounces to the yard. It provides the crispness of tropical worsteds, the lustrous gabardines and broadcloths, and the softness of knitted sweaters and other articles of clothing.

The study of wool is a study of paradoxes which fit with remarkable accuracy into the demands we make on the clothes we wear. The natural water-repellent skin of the fiber, together with the resilience and hairiness of wool, provides a surface which encourages rain drops to roll off without wetting the fabric. On the other hand, the water absorbent interior of the fiber will soak up, in the form of water vapor, quantities of moisture exuded by the body. If this moisture is not absorbed, it collects in the fabric forming a soggy mass that drags stickily against the skin while it conducts body heat away to the outside air.

Much has been written in general terms about the

natural properties of wool, but we are entering an age where there is increasing interest in the specific—and in the "why" of fabric performance. We are a test-tube worshipping nation and are prone to clamor for innovations. When we see a new characteristic, we forget to check on other quality components which we have come to assume as a matter of course. No one characteristic, indeed no two or three selected characteristics by themselves, controls the ultimate usefulness of a fiber when it is made up into a garment.

Each fiber presents a combination of many properties and the usefulness of the fiber depends upon how well ALL of these properties fit into the pattern of qualities required. The same property change which improves one characteristic of performance may impair another characteristic. An increase of fiber strength will increase the resistance to fabric tear only when it is accompanied by the extensibility which, in the case of the wool fiber, distributes damaging loads among many individual fibers. Moreover, the increased strength of a fiber may serve to hold tightly to the surface of a fabric the short loose fibers which slip out during wear and cause the unsightly fuzz balls called pilling.

Much emphasis is placed on the assumption that the good points of a fiber may be divorced from the bad ones by the simple expedient of blending. It is assumed that the resultant mixture includes all of the good properties of each fiber and none of the bad. It is true that skillful blending may bring out and emphasize the better qualities of the different fibers and minimize the worst, but this result must be independently proved for each blend, in each construction, and in each use. Blending therefore is hardly the all-inclusive panacea it is sometimes represented to be.

Each end use of a fabric has its own individual pattern of requirements. This has long been recognized and is the reason why such a great variety of fabric constructions, weights, and finishes has been developed. Construction and finishing treatments can do much to adapt any one fiber to a range of performances. When a fiber is as versatile as wool and combines so many of the necessary properties, a suitable selection of constructions and finishes can provide a phenomenal choice of end products suited to a tremendous assortment of functional demands, personal tastes, and styles. Furthermore, in any one construction and finish, the pattern of fiber properties is so adaptable that an individual fabric may be appropriate for numerous uses.

The intelligent selection and engineering of all fibers to secure their maximum contribution to human requirements will eventually react to the benefit of society as a whole. Scientists and engineers are making constant progress in improving fibers and methods of processing them into textiles. Meanwhile, there is little comprehensive information available to consumers or their impartial advisors as to their actual utility qualities of wear, launderability, cleanability, and resistance to damage under normal conditions of service. Advertising, even when conscientiously controlled, must be too brief and too much simplified to provide useful background for critical selection. Promotional literature too often presents only the most favorable characteristics and leaves the consumer to discover the unfavorable ones for herself. Both are so weighted in volume and force of presentation that their impact on the consumer reflects more closely the relative size of promotional budgets than the inherent worth of the materials offered. Retail sales personnel and the public are as confused today as the retail buyer. This confusion is shared by the textile manufacturer and the apparel producer.

Part One

What We Know About the Wool Fiber

What We Know About the Wool Fiber

Many reference books are available on the chemistry and physics of wool, but we will leave the academic considerations to the scientists, the engineers, and the students. There are, however, many extremely interesting points about wool which have a direct relationship with its performance. It is always helpful to understand why and how a certain quality is provided. Indeed the scientists working in entirely different fields have begun to study the complex behavior of wool fibers to help them understand phenomena in bacteriology, animal muscles, and even cancer growth. The mechanism which enables wool fiber to provide crease resistance and warmth in a winter coat has been found to be identical with that which enables bacterial flagella to swim or a muscle to contract in moving an arm or a leg.

The most important characteristics of wool which give satisfaction in a blanket, a suit, or a pair of socks are extensibility, elasticity, absorption, felting, and chemical activity. These technical terms will be explained more explicitly as we come to them. They are of interest here only as they comprise a listing of the major fiber properties providing texture, resilience, warmth, fit, durability, wrinkle resistance, and dyeing qualities which have made wool so popular over the ages. In fact, the majority of the vital and distinctive characteristics of woolen or worsted fabrics depend heavily on combinations of these properties.

The Fiber We See

As a beginning we will consider the wool fiber as it appears to the naked eye. It is a long fiber which resembles a fine hair. Looking at wool in a large mass, we see that it has a soft, rich luster and is usually white or slightly yellow, though some types may be black or brown. Other colors have been produced experimentally by feeding special diets to the sheep, and even striped brown wool has been grown in this way; but these are of academic interest only.

If we have several types of wool to choose from, we will find that the wool fibers come in different lengths; some are finer than others and the degree of luster ranges from a dull bloom of little reflectance to a silky gloss.

We also see that the fibers do not lie straight. Some fibers, particularly the finer ones, have a pronounced crimp, others have a less obvious crimp and some show only occasional bends or a slight curl. Fibers lying together on a smooth table will not compress to a tightly packed mass, but will repel each other. Even when we press them together they spring apart when released. This characteristic is known as resilience and it gives wool its loft which produces open, porous fabrics of high covering power and thick, warm fabrics with a minimum of weight.

Even the most gentle pull will straighten out its crimp or natural curl. Release one end and the crimp or curl springs back in place.

"Even when we press (wool fibers) together they spring apart when released."

If we take a firm grip on the two ends, and after first stretching the curl or crimp out of the fiber we pull a little harder, even the straightened fiber can be elongated. If we can get a good enough hold on the fiber, we

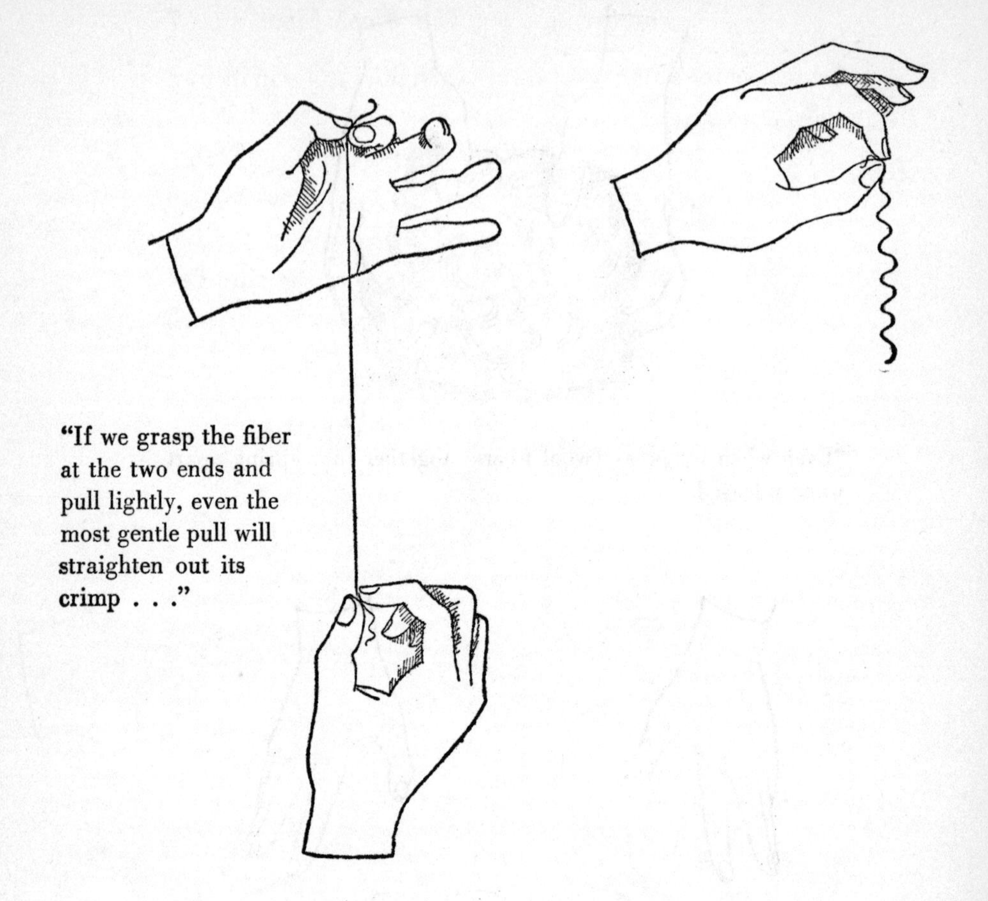

"If we grasp the fiber at the two ends and pull lightly, even the most gentle pull will straighten out its crimp . . ."

can stretch it as much as one-third of its original length before it is ruptured. When we release the stretching force, the fiber will spring back just as when we released the fiber we had uncrimped. This demonstrates elasticity, elastic recovery, or resilience.

So far, without any equipment except our eyes and hands, we have learned considerable that is important about the fiber. We know that it comes in a variety of lengths, finenesses, and lusters, and with a number of types and degrees of crimp. We know also that the fibers are inclined to repel one another so they lie free because the resilience of the wool forces each fiber to lie in its own special position.

Let us now look at the fiber a little more closely, with a magnifying glass. If we examine a highly crimped fiber, such as a Merino, we see that the crimp is not a simple wave in one plane, but is in three dimensions. The form of the crimp is illustrated in the drawing which shows that instead of a series of repeated bends in one plane, the crimp rises and falls in three dimensions. In the same diagram it can be seen that the fiber is oval, not

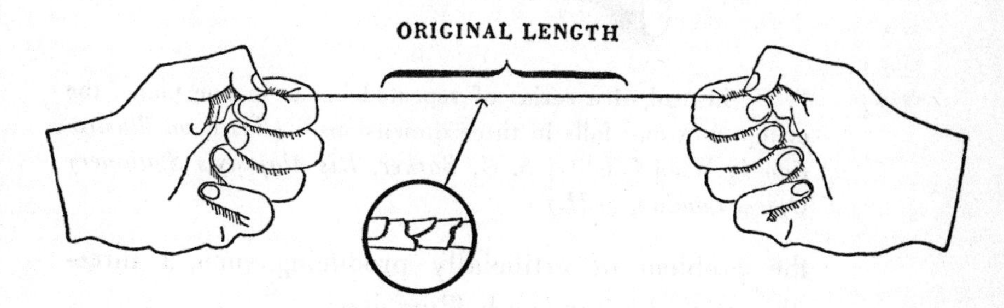

"... we can stretch (wool) as much as one-third of its original length before it is ruptured."

round, and that this oval cross section twists and turns as we pass down the fiber. If the fibers were crimped in one plane, they could quite conceivably lie closely packed side by side in a yarn. On the other hand, such a three-dimensional crimp is much more effective in providing and maintaining loft, or a large bulk for a given number or weight of fibers.

Wool is the only apparel fiber which has a natural crimp. Other fibers may be artificially crimped, but this artificial crimp is usually set in a single plane and

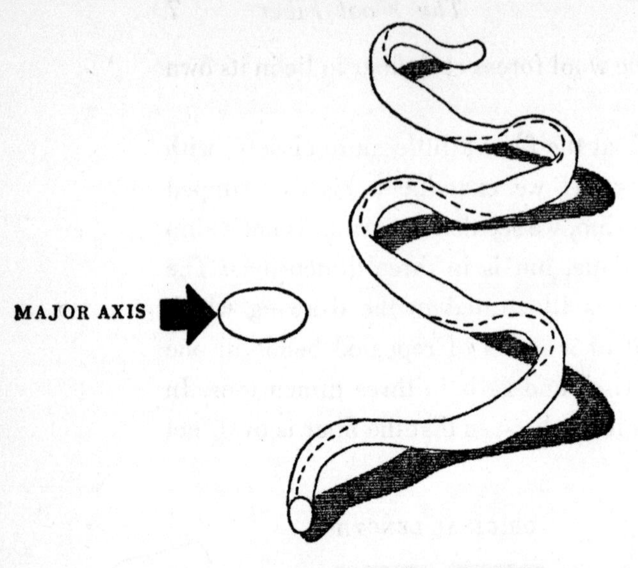

". . . instead of a series of repeated bends in one plane, the crimp rises and falls in three dimensions." (*Based on illustration in* Wool Quality, *S. G. Barker, His Majesty's Stationery Office, London, 1931.*)

the problem of artificially producing such a three-dimensional crimp is a baffling one.

When we discuss the wool fiber we are not talking about any one shape or dimension, but a whole range of shapes and dimensions which can be chosen from the sheep of the world according to the special purpose for which it is to be used. Through the centuries, sheep have been selected and crossbred to produce wools required in an increasing variety to meet humanity's widening and changing demands. These wools are indeed a far cry from the primitive wools of the Dark Ages. It is interesting to note just how wide is today's choice of wools for an infinite number of uses.

Fiber Measurement

Wool fibers are grown in lengths from one and one-half

to fourteen inches. The shorter wools are used chiefly in woolens where we want a maximum of fiber tangle and rough, hairy surfaces. The longer fibers are also used in woolens, but their chief use is in producing worsteds. In the worsted process the fibers are combed out to lie parallel and each fiber is held closely to the yarn surface by twisting the yarn tightly. This gives strong, smooth yarns and fine-textured, smooth-finished fabrics.

When we endeavor to measure the fineness of wool we get beyond the capacity of the naked eye. We can see that some fibers are coarser than others and we must resort to the microscope to measure these differences. Actually the diameter of the wool fiber can be expressed in thousandths of an inch, but it is more convenient to express it in a much smaller unit called the micron. One micron is about one twenty-five-thousandth of an inch or, expressing it another way, about forty millionths of an inch.

The mills pay a great deal of attention to fineness when they select their wools. The wool buyers class wools according to the finest yarn count which can be spun from a given stock, but the scientists rely on actual diameter measurements. They find that wools are available in diameters all the way from 10 to 70 microns.

The crimp in wools varies roughly according to fineness of fibers. Some wools have practically no crimp at all and others contain as many as 22 to 30 crimps per inch.

The Effect of Time, Temperature and Moisture

We have said that wool fiber could be extended or stretched up to 30 per cent of its length before it is broken. We must amplify this. Wool fiber behaves differently according to the amount of moisture present. Although it may break at around 30-per cent extension in normal indoor conditions, it can be stretched as much as 60 per cent if the fiber is wet. One of the very interesting things about wool is that atmospheric conditions influence its behavior. Time influences its behavior, too. If you hold the fiber stretched for a period of an hour or more, its recovery is slower than if you stretch it quickly and immediately let go.

Actually wool has three kinds of recovery or resilience. There is the "immediate elastic recovery," the springing back to its original form immediately a deforming force is removed. This is the quality which promises a wrinkle-free suit and maintains the thickness and insulation value of a blanket. Secondly, there is "delayed recovery" which requires an interval of time for recovery from severe distortions or deformations which have existed for long periods. Delayed recovery is utilized when we hang clothing overnight and find the more serious wrinkles gone in the morning. A third form of recovery is that which is accomplished by allowing a fiber to relax in a humid atmosphere. This type of recovery eliminates distortions (or creases) which have been set by holding the wet fiber or fabric in a distorted condition until it dries. We utilize the "set" when we crease and press our garments, and we utilize the recovery when we steam a coat or skirt over a bathtub of hot water to encourage moisture-set wrinkles to "hang out."

Of all the fibers, wool is the most susceptible to moisture, time and temperature influences. This is an extremely important characteristic. By a suitable manipulation of these three factors, we have developed many very useful practices for the manufacture and care of our woolen and worsted fabrics and garments. Indeed, most of the garment-care practices which require an iron, and particularly those which employ moisture, are based on the very convenient time, temperature and moisture sensitivity of wool.

But wool is unique in another way. Most fibers which are absorbent lose much of their elasticity or resilience

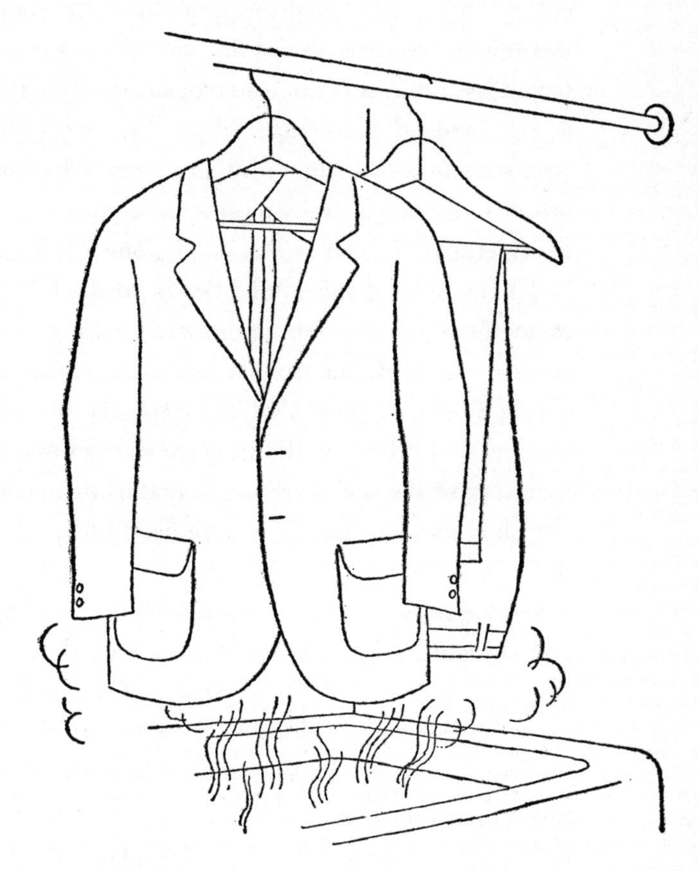

"A third form of recovery . . . is accomplished by allowing a fiber to relax in a humid atmosphere . . . we utilize (this) recovery when we steam a coat or skirt over a bathtub of hot water . . ."

when wet. In contrast, wool retains its resilience and liveliness when it is wet. This is a very valuable quality.

Physical Structure

We have been looking at wool through the microscope since 1665. As our techniques have developed and our optical equipment improved, we have learned a great deal about the structure of the wool fiber. First of all, we have found that it is not a homogeneous cylinder such as is obtained in man-made fibers by extrusion through spinnerets. On the contrary, it is a structure which is built up of a number of units of several distinct types, just as a skyscraper is built of steel and stone and glass.

The outside of the wool fiber is covered with a layer of scales which overlap one another with their free ends pointing toward the tip of the fiber. These scales are characteristic of wool and are partially responsible for the fact that a fiber will slip more easily toward the root than toward the tip. Conversely, materials in contact with the fiber will slip or slide more easily toward the tip of the fiber.

On the back of the sheep this difference of friction in two directions encourages particles of dust, sand and even burrs to work their way out of the fleece. This frictional difference, tip-to-root vs. root-to-tip, is also a factor in giving wool its very valuable and unique felting power because it causes the fibers to travel and tangle as the wet fabric is worked mechanically. This property is utilized in creating many of the special textures we value in woolen and worsted fabrics. This same felting power, when uncontrolled, is responsible for the irreversible

"The outside of the wool fiber is covered with a layer of scales which overlap one another with their free ends pointing toward the tip of the fiber."

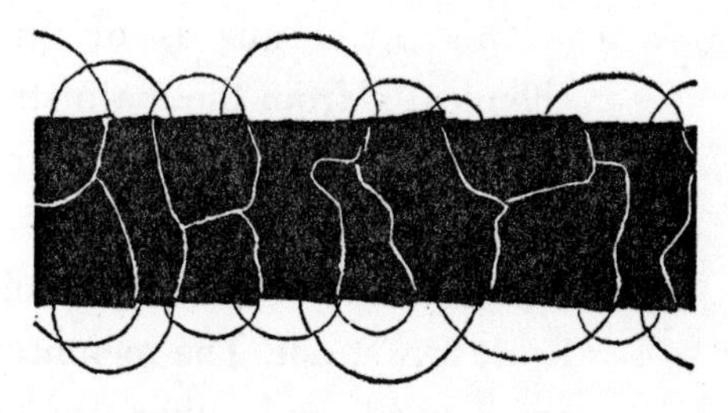

"Scientists had observed that small bubbles appeared on the surface of these scales when wool was treated with chlorine water."

felting shrinkage that takes place when we throw a luxurious wool sweater in the washing machine along with the family sheets.

For a long time there was a mystery about the outer surface of these scales. Scientists had observed that small bubbles appeared on the surface of the scales when wool was treated with chlorine water. We knew these bubbles, or sacs, were hollow because when one touched the sac with the point of a dull needle it could be seen under a microscope that the sac was indented easily. However, the skin of these sacs was so thin that it could not be examined even with high-powered lenses. It was only when a new instrument was developed, the electron microscope, that it has become possible to study this skin.

We now know that there is an outer skin or membrane which lies over the surface of all the scales. We are not sure whether this membrane, called the epicuticle, covers the entire fiber or separate membranes protect each scale. At any rate, the membrane appears to be attached at the edges of the scales. This is the only non-protein constituent of the fiber and is much more resistant to chemical action. The protein can be dissolved away by suitable chemical solvents and a hollow tube of skin remains.

This membrane is of an entirely different nature chemically from the main structure of the fiber. In particular, the membrane appears to be of a water repellent nature, so that liquid water is not attracted to the surface of the fiber, and a bundle of clean wool fibers is very difficult to wet out. The membrane does become broken by mechanical and other treatments, and the more the surface of the fiber is damaged, the more wettable does the fiber become.

The presence of this skin on the fiber explains one of the paradoxes of wool. Even though liquid water is repelled by the surface of the fiber, water vapor can penetrate the membrane and reach the interior of the fiber, which has a strong affinity for water. Thus, wool clothes will take up the moisture of the body in the form of water vapor, without feeling damp. This moisture is then released slowly to the outside atmosphere, which prevents sudden chills. Wool clothing will repel a short rain shower, at the same time allowing the body moisture to reach the outside atmosphere.

This outer structure of scales and their protecting membrane is called the cuticle. The cuticle surrounds an inner structure, called the cortex, which is made up of millions of small spindles called cortical cells. They are somewhat thicker in the middle and taper to a fine point at each end. They are packed so tightly together that they are flattened where they touch one another. The spindles,

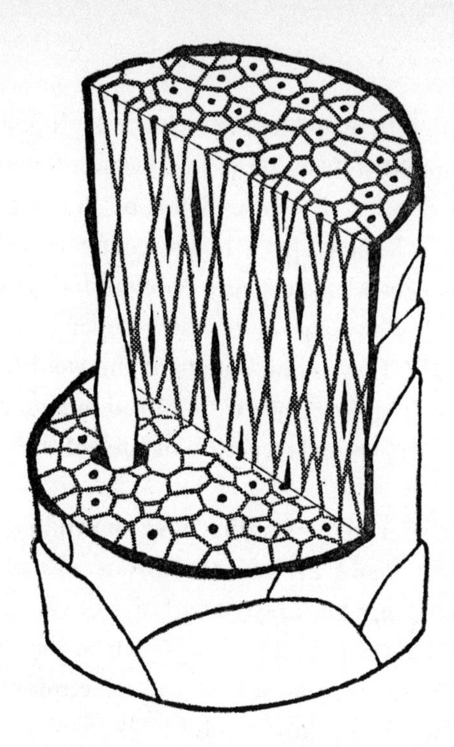

"The cuticle surrounds an inner structure, called the cortex, which is made up of millions of small spindles called cortical cells."

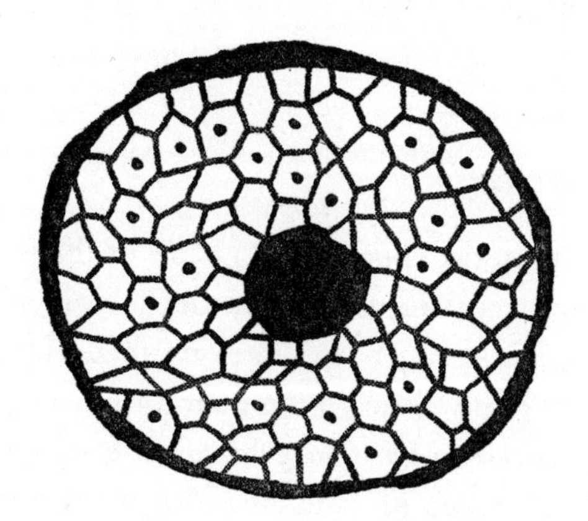

"Some of the coarser wool fibers have a hollow space in the center called the medulla."

or cortical cells, can be seen with a high-powered microscope and are from 100 to 200 microns long and from 2 to 5 microns wide. Some of the coarser wool fibers have a hollow space in the center called the medulla. This central space may be completely open or it may be filled with a loose network of open cell walls like a honeycomb. These components of the wool fiber structure are cemented together with a protein material which resembles the chemical structure of each of the individual units.

Electron-microscope studies have shown that the cortical cells are made up of fine fibrous elements called fibrils which, in turn, are really bundles of still smaller elements. The ultimate division is termed the protofibril. At 65,000 times magnification, electron-microscope photographs show these protofibrils as consisting of globular particles so small that we measure their diameter in wave lengths of light. Some research workers think that these globular particles may actually be the keratin molecules, but now we are getting into the chemical structure of wool.

Chemical Sructure

When we study the chemical structure of the wool fiber, we must set the microscope aside and rely on other techniques. The X-ray has been a very useful tool, but we do not send the X-ray through the fiber and study an image similar to that seen by a surgeon when he studies bones in the body. Instead of a shadow picture, we get what is called a diffraction diagram which is really a code picture of light and shadows. We throw beams of X-rays into the fiber and they are bounced off layers of atoms lying in particular planes onto a photographic film giving us excellent clues that can be interpreted by means of physics and mathematics to tell us the shape and arrangement of the molecules which would cause the scattered pattern we obtain.

Another system of investigation depends upon the study of chemical reactions of wool to other materials. Chemical analysis has shown us that wool contains carbon, hydrogen, nitrogen, oxygen, and sulphur. This knowledge alone, however, gives us little information about how these very common elements are united. It is important to know how they are arranged because their behavior depends just as much on the combinations in which they lie as on the elements which are present. Much can be learned about the nature of the chemical arrangement by studying the way in which various chemicals react to the wool fiber.

Here again we find paradoxes. Wool can act as either an acid or an alkali which means that both alkalies and acids will react to it. The scientists describe this as amphoteric. Furthermore, the wool molecule contains many different types of active chemical groups so that a large number of different types of chemicals will unite with it. This is the reason so many different classes of dyestuffs can be securely anchored to the wool fiber by chemical combinations.

With the exception of the outer sheath or membrane protecting the scales, wool is a protein. There are many proteins associated with living substances, but wool is a special kind of protein called keratin. Other keratinaceous materials closely resembling wool are human hair, fingernails, and the skin.

The wool molecule is very long and flexible and is referred to as a chain molecule because it consists of long chains of atoms and groups of atoms. Like all chain molecules used in nature, it is extremely complicated. It is believed that the various components of the wool fiber structure, that is the scales, the cortical cells, and the cementing material between them, are all made up of the same type of molecules and that the difference is in their arrangement within the structure.

The backbone of this molecular chain is a series of carbon and nitrogen atoms. These atoms are held together by strong chemical bonds, but they are more or less free to rotate without separation. The chain can be twisted into all sorts of positions. Although this might sound very simple, it is one of the fundamental principles of life. Nature has utilized this principle in a most amazing fashion. Our bodies and at least the solid part of most living things are largely fibers of one type or another and these fibers are made from different types of chain molecules. The flexibility of these fibers and the chain molecules which form them is the foundation for elasticity and movement of living bodies.

The wool molecule has become outstandingly important because it has taught the scientists so much about proteins in general. X-ray analyses of wool protein revealed the nature of biological elasticity. As a result, important biochemical, biological, and medical advances have resulted. It can be said justly that wool is as distinguished a fiber scientifically as it is a vital factor in our social and industrial life.

Nature has developed different types of chains for different chemical purposes, but she has also developed many systems of folding and unfolding these chains to do her will. For example, let us consider the remarkable long-range elasticity which is characteristic of wool. As you know, damp wool, if left alone, will recover its original form. The means by which it does so is the same molecular mechanism by which we move our arms and legs; that is, the repeated coiling up and straightening out of chain molecules.

The great extensibility of unvulcanized rubber is frequently used for illustrative purposes. You can stretch it easily to many times its length. For a long time we had no explanation for its behavior, but now we know that the chain molecules in rubber are coiled up when the rubber is in the unstretched condition. When it is stretched the chains uncoil.

But in rubber the chains are coiled at random instead of in orderly controlled folds as in wool and muscle tissues. The haphazard arrangement of molecules in rubber could never meet the exacting demands which we place on wool and muscle. This property is one of wool's most valuable assets. The wool fiber is determined to return to its natural shape when given an opportunity.

The chain molecules of keratin lie normally in wavy lines. It is then called *alpha*-keratin and the regular folds are called the *alpha*-folds. They are molecular "crimps" if you prefer to describe them that way, but it should be kept in mind that these crimps have nothing to do with the visible crimps in the fiber itself. The keratin chains are crimped whether or not the fiber is crimped. And furthermore, they are far smaller; in fact they are invisible under the microscope.

If we should want to consider wool fiber as a mechanical device, we could picture its crimped chain molecules as a series of minute springs. When the fiber is pulled they elongate, and when the molecules are completely straight they are just about twice as long as in their natural coiled position. This would indicate that the theoretical maximum extensibility of wool fiber would be about 100 per cent.

The molecular chains used in the construction of all natural proteins, including wool protein or keratin, are classed under the chemical name of polypeptide chains. Their thickness is not more than one 25-millionth of an inch, so a tremendous number can lie side by side even in the finest fiber. Generally they run lengthwise with the fiber and are connected together at regular intervals by cross connections or chemical bonds. If we could see them they would look rather like ladders with cross connections as rungs, and the longitudinal members bent into a regular crimp or fold. When the folds are pulled out the cross links help pull the main chains back into the folded position again. If, however, the folds are kept straightened for a long time, new rungs or cross links are formed which will oppose refolding and thus create "delayed recovery."

The principles we have described can be applied to animal and human hairs, as well as wool. All are composed of keratin with the same molecular plan of crimped elastic chains. The scales on the wool fiber are more prominent than on hair, but hair and wool fibers are the same in their fundamental properties. They stretch and return to their natural form the same way and can be given permanent set in the same way.

As has been pointed out, the molecular crimp should not be confused with the crimp in the fiber itself. On the other hand, the crimp or wave in the molecules has a great deal to do with the action of the crimp in the fiber.

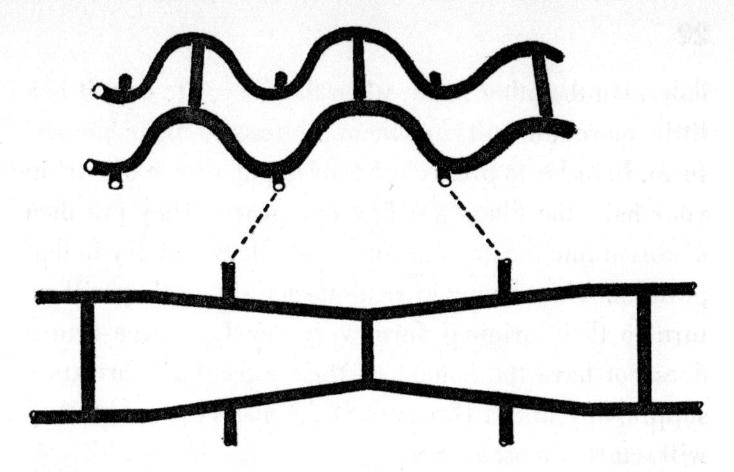

"If we could see (the molecular chains) they would look rather like ladders with cross connections as rungs, and the longitudinal members bent into a regular crimp or fold. When the folds are pulled out the cross links help pull the main chains back into the folded position again."

When you bend a fiber the outside of the curve is stretched to some extent and the molecular chains are partially unfolded. The tendency of these chains in the stretched portion of the fiber to resume their normal position exerts the force which will bring the fiber back into its original form.

Wool that is highly crimped or hair which is naturally curly is in effect deformed when stretched to a straight position. In this case the molecular chains which are on the inside of the waves are unfolded when the fiber is straightened, and their desire to return to their folded position produces the force which returns a crimped fiber to its natural state after it has been straightened.

When wool and hair are dry it is more difficult to stretch them than when they are wet. Water acts as a sort of molecular lubricant for the movement of the molecules. On the other hand, when the fibers are dry, it is a little more difficult for them to resume their normal form. In order to press clothes or to put a wave or curl in your hair, the fibers are first dampened. They are then distorted into the desired form and allowed to dry in that position. After drying in an abnormal shape, they will return to their original form very slowly, as the return does not have the benefit of this molecular lubrication supplied by water. However, if the fibers are rewet, they will return almost at once.

While wool is a unique textile fiber, it represents only one illustration of a molecular principle used by nature. Another very interesting illustration is to be found in muscles. Wool and muscle are similar in their structure, but for a long time we did not understand just how similar they are.

Muscles always act through the process of shortening themselves. Wool also can be shortened fairly easily to two-thirds its normal length. We did not know this until recently. When we found out how to do it we called the phenomenon supercontraction. Supercontraction is accomplished by steaming the stretched fiber for only one or two minutes and then removing the stretching force but leaving the steam on. The exposure of the stretched

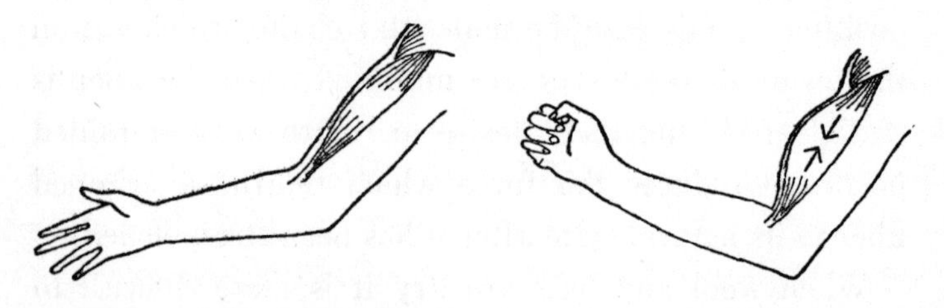

"Muscles always act through the process of shortening themselves."

fiber to steam for a very short period breaks some of the cross linkages. With these cross links broken, the fiber is free to contract to a length shorter than its original length.

On the other hand, if the fiber is stretched in steam for more than a minute or two, it begins to adjust itself in the new position or takes on "permanent set" by the formation of new bonds between the chains. We had been doing just this for centuries in pressing clothes and curling hair and it was not until someone tried the short-interval steam stretching that we discovered supercontraction and the missing link between wool and muscle behavior.

The scientific fields of biochemistry, biology and medicine have learned many fundamental lessons from the study of wool because wool was the first structure demonstrated to have a systematic folding of its protein chains. Now that these other sciences have advanced so far, the situation is reversed and we are learning about wool from many non-textile researches.

The bacteriologists have been interested for years in a special structure called bacterial flagellum. Flagella are whiplike threads or tails which propel bacteria by means of a lashing motion. They can be seen through the electron microscope. The chain molecules running along flagella are not only folded in the normal pattern, as found in wool, but can be folded into a supercontracted form, as in a shortened muscle or in wool supercontracted with steam. The flagellar movement is caused by a wave of chain foldings that passes along one side shortening them in respect to the chains on the other side. The actual wave motion is probably spiral.

In our studies of the chemical or molecular structure of the wool fiber, it has been possible to learn much about how this very special molecular form gives wool its natural resilience and explains the effect of moisture and stretching in providing permanent set. All of these characteristics or phenomena have an extremely important effect on the value of wool because they give wool its unique type of resilience which is so important in the qualities we expect in woolen and worsted fabrics.

We have seen that the phenomena and mechanisms which control wool's behavior are the identical mechanisms which are basic in many of nature's processes. These mechanisms continue to act long after the fiber has been extruded from the skin of the sheep, and long after the fiber has been clipped from the sheep's back.

Part Two

The Quality Characteristics of Woolen and Worsted Fabrics

The Quality Characteristics of Woolen and Worsted Fabrics

The common qualities which we demand in varying proportions in all apparel fabrics can be divided into a number of classifications as shown below.

1. Texture and Hand
2. Fit, Shape Retention and Tailoring
3. Wrinkle Resistance
4. Color
5. Soil Resistance
6. Cleaning
7. Durability
8. Warmth
9. Comfort in Warm Weather
10. Rain Repellency
11. Flame Resistance

We can understand just why wool has earned its popular place in our economic and social structure when we realize that all of these important fabric qualities depend to a high degree on wool's unique combination of fiber properties; extensibility, resilience, absorption, felting, and chemical activity. Even in these properties wool's irregularities fit with remarkable closeness the complex combinations of qualities required to provide the satisfaction we have learned to expect. For example, the high extensions of wool are proportionately more easily obtained than low extensions; or expressing it another way, wool becomes more pliable as the degree of stretch (or bend) is increased. Wool's resilience is greatest after low distortions which happen to be the distortions usually encountered in service. Wool has an extremely high absorption capacity for water vapor, but a low rate of absorption for liquid water. This paradox allows for the disposal of perspiration and gives reasonable protection in a sudden shower.

The discussion to follow will show just why all this is true.

Texture and Hand

In this discussion, texture is considered to include the appearance characteristics of the fabric surface and the way the fabric behaves in manipulation, such as its drape and its flexibility. Hand includes the sensation against the skin and the subjective reaction to the fabric when crushed between the fingers.

There are a number of basic characteristics of wool which, together with the craftsmanship developed through the ages, make it possible to provide an extremely wide range of texture effects. For example, the high resilience of wool, coupled with its natural crimp, prevents the fibers from packing. This insures lofty* yarns and porous fabrics. Wool fibers tend to repel each other to give the maximum openness permitted with a specified twist or closeness of weave. This characteristic allows for an easy rearrangement of the fibers in relation to each other as the fabric is distorted in service or handling. This fiber rearrangement in the yarns and yarn movement in the fabric can be utilized to produce a soft, flexible hand and to reduce the deformation and, hence, the abuse of the individual fiber.

If smoothness or firmness of hand is desired, the natural openness of the woolen yarn can be counteracted by several common manufacturing practices. First of all the wool can be selected for length. Wool comes in a tremendous variety of staple lengths, all the way from 1½ inches to 14 inches according to type. Long lengths allow

* High bulk or volume for a given weight.

(a) woolen yarn

(b) worsted yarn

"Wool fibers tend to repel each other to give the maximum openness permitted with a specified twist. . . . If smoothness or firmness of hand is desired, . . . (long fibers can) be locked together through many revolutions of twist . . . (and) we can comb the fibers to dispose of the shorter fibers and force the longer fibers to lie parallel."

the individual fibers to be locked together through many revolutions of twist in the yarn. Second, we can comb the fibers to dispose of the shorter fibers and force the longer fibers to lie parallel. Third, we can manipulate the construction specifications by tightly twisting the yarns and weaving closely to give extremely firm, smooth-finished worsteds. Fine worsted yarns are used to make fabrics for sheer evening dresses and light-weight, smartly tailored business suits and dresses.

While all types of wool are inclined to resist close packing, the tendency to produce loft is accentuated by the presence of high crimp. Wool is, of course, the only fiber which has a natural and permanent crimp. The crimp is three dimensional, an effect very difficult to reproduce artificially. In this characteristic there is also a wide range for selection among the many types of wool. Some types have practically no crimp at all while the very fine wools have as many as 22 to 30 crimps per inch. Crimp influences the loft or openness of the yarns, and also increases the frequency of fiber-to-fiber contact. As the yarn is stretched the crimped fibers can be straightened with very little force, but a recovery force still remains within the fiber that seeks to restore this crimp. Crimp is responsible for many of the very unique characteristics of hand, softness, and drape of woolen and worsted fabrics.

The apparent softness or stiffness of a fabric and the way a fabric hangs or drapes are controlled by the selection of fibers and the manufacturing specifications. In any one type of fiber, fibers of large diameter produce a stiffer handle compared with the fine fibers which impart softness from their shape influence alone. Here again wool is available in a wide variety of types ranging in fiber diameter from 10 to 70 microns. A micron is about one twenty-five-thousandth or forty millionths of an inch.

But these simple influences of dimension and shape are only a part of the story. Wool fibers show a very interesting behavior as they are stretched or twisted. Remember that when you crush a fabric some of the fibers may be bent, others may be rotated or twisted, and some may be stretched as they seek to find their appropriate place in the distorted fabric. We must therefore consider the way fibers distort, the ease with which they can be bent, twisted, or extended, beyond the simple effect of their shape or of geometry.

Wool has a unique behavior pattern as it is distorted progressively. It seems relatively stiff when touched lightly but on being grasped firmly it feels soft and pliable; thus wool is crisp without harshness. The physicists point out that this is due to the peculiar stress-strain curve of the fiber which indicates high resistance to distortion under low loads and low resistance, proportionately, under high loads.

In some types of fabrics a hairy surface is desired. Such surfaces provide interesting and novel appearance effects to amplify style possibilities and also encourage rain repellency—as will be discussed in another section. When we wish to accentuate the hairiness of a fabric surface we select the woolen system of manufacture, which calls for a high proportion of short fibers with a loose twist and produces a light, bulky yarn with a large number of free fiber ends projecting. Such hairy surfaces impart the feeling of warmth to the touch since they reduce the area of contact with the skin. Unlike other absorbent fibers the resilience of wool is unimpaired even when wet, and so the surface texture effects and warmth to the touch are maintained under both wet and dry conditions.

Socks represent an application where texture is of special importance. Wool socks used to be worn primarily for warmth. However, as shrink-resisting socks have become available we find woolen socks worn throughout the year. The absorption of wool keeps the feet dry even in summer and the natural cushioning of a wool sock has been welcomed by most men. Socks should maintain a good cushioning action under the constantly repeated compressions of walking and the sustained compression of standing. The texture should be such that it does not irritate or abrade the skin nor should it hold unsightly lint by static attraction or develop pills in repeated wear. Fibers which pack together in the yarn soon become most uncomfortable on the feet. With such fibers every wale or unevenness of the knitted construction forms a hard lump to develop calluses or blisters on the tender skin. Wool does not pack and condense and wool socks always provide a soft dry cushion for the feet.

In some fabrics, such as blankets or sports clothes, we desire to create a surface in which the appearance of the yarn structure is minimized or hidden under a light fluffy nap. The resilience and toughness of wool fibers readily lend woolen structures to napping in which short ends of fibers are teased out of their yarns to produce, after shearing, an even surface comprised entirely of individual fibers extending beyond the yarns in the fabric base.

Among all of the peculiar properties of wool its ability to felt is one of its most valuable. Indeed many fabrics are manufactured by the utilization of this quality alone without recourse to spinning or weaving. Such fabrics, called mechanical felts, are used to cushion machinery, in the construction of delicate precision parts for pianos, as boot liners, for hats, washers, shock and sound absorbing mediums, decorative materials, and even some types of apparel. In their manufacture this unique felting power of wool provides the entire binding power in structures ranging from light, soft pads to materials which are as

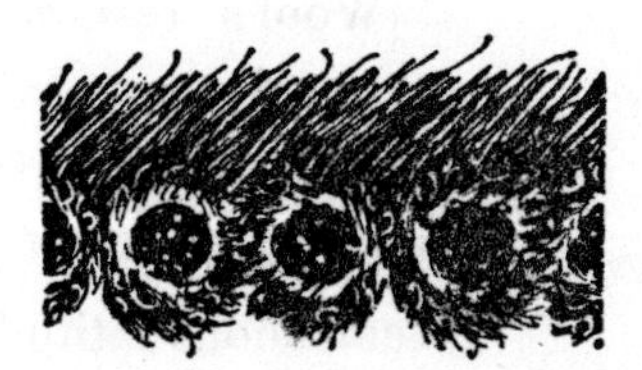

"The resilience and toughness of wool fibers readily lend woolen structures to napping in which short ends of fibers are teased out of their yarns . . ."

hard, tough, and horny as buffalo hide. It is only necessary to "work" the wool in certain chemicals until the desired strength, toughness, and stiffness are obtained.

The remarkable felting power of wool is also used in conjunction with weaving. Woven fabrics can be made more dense and firm by the use of a mild, carefully controlled form of felting which is more commonly called fulling. In fulling, the cloth is manipulated in certain chemicals to tangle the individual fibers in the yarns and lock them together, thus increasing the density. Carried to extremes, fabrics made with lofty, open yarns can be increased in density so radically that the woven structure is all but obliterated. On the other hand, gentle fulling may be employed to give an increased firmness of handle without any obvious alteration of the pattern of weave as in serges. More complete felting or fulling is employed to create soft doeskins, heavy meltons, and kerseys.

Sometimes novel and interesting texture effects are provided by mixing special wools. Lambs wool, for example, contains a range of fiber types from the soft down-like undercoat to long irregular hairy fibers on the surface of the fleece. Lambs wool and special blends of wools of widely different types, such as cashmere, mohair, and camels hair, are employed to give novelty effects for special textures.

Wool's resilience, pliability, crimp, unique stress-strain characteristics, felting power, and the wide range of fiber length, finenesses, and crimp frequencies all combine to give the fabric designer and the finisher tremendous latitude in creating texture effects.

Fit, Shape Retention and Tailoring

There is much that a good tailor can do to make a garment fit well, but he is limited by the characteristics of the fabric he is handling. Clothes are not worn on a rigid form like the department-store dummy. The body moves constantly and some of the frequent changes in position—such as sitting down, reaching, and stooping—involve radical changes in the shape of a garment.

If a fabric is difficult to stretch, body movements must be allowed for by providing a looseness which in many cases gives an objectionable appearance, adds bulk, and detracts from trimness. The potato sack effect is approached rapidly.

The ability of wool to stretch is, of course, well known. Individual fibers can be stretched 30 per cent without rupturing and, in addition, the resistance of wool fibers to close packing in the yarns affords a liberal opportunity for the fabric to adjust to body positions with a minimum of distortion of the fiber itself. Because of this quality, wool garments may be tailored to fit as snugly as style demands. Wool socks can be drawn over the heel and still fit closely at the ankle.

When fullness is desired the natural draping qualities of wool assure an attractive softness of contour and gracefulness of folds. As wool absorbs moisture readily static is not a problem. If wool were nonabsorbent it would take on a high static charge which would cause the

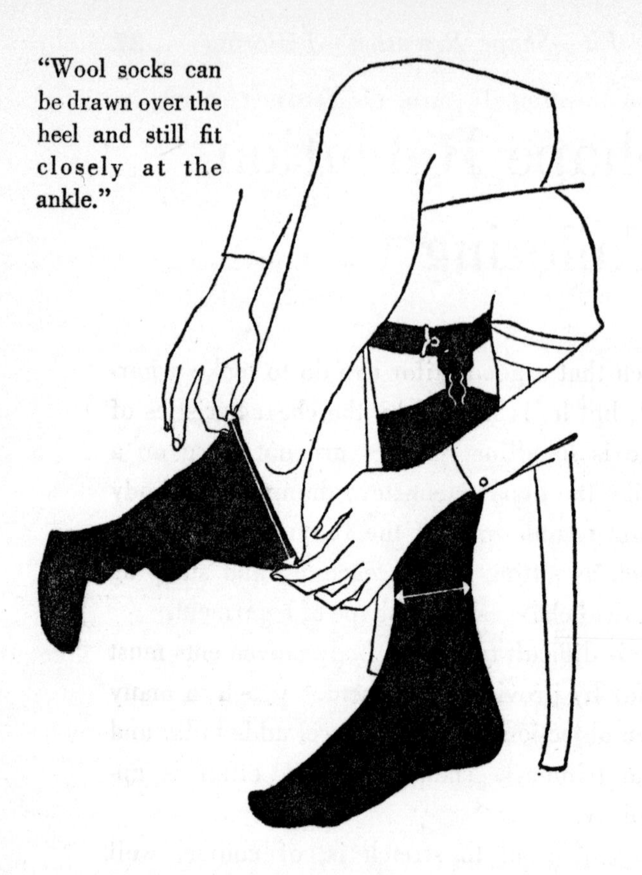
"Wool socks can be drawn over the heel and still fit closely at the ankle."

fabric to cling to the figure in a disagreeable manner.

But the mere ability of a material to stretch with body movements is not enough. The fabric must recover from such distortions whether they are rapidly repeated when one is walking or maintained for considerable periods when one is seated. As the fabric is distorted, the yarns and fibers in the yarns are bent and stretched. They also seek to rearrange themselves in the fabric structure to minimize the required change in fiber and yarn. When the distorting force is removed, the resilience of the individual fibers restores them to their original form and position. In turn, the fabric recovers its former loft and texture.

The scientists have measured the resilience of fibers in a number of ways. Most people are already aware of the resilience of wool as they wear it in garments, but the technical men are not content with qualitative ideas. They want figures, actual test results which they can use for evaluation of even small differences.

A laboratory test is quite different from the impression you get from actual use. You obtain your impression after long contact with a fiber in many types of fabrics used in a wide variety of situations. Obviously, actual experience is the final proof of value and the objective of laboratory tests is to anticipate what the reaction from long-term use will be.

However, laboratory tests have several important uses. When tests can be interpreted in terms of actual service, individual lots can be checked against a standard, new fibers can be appraised provisionally before there is adequate service experience to make a final evaluation, and the comparisons are quantitative.

In comparing resilience in the laboratory we must make several very important choices. For example, what type of resilience is of major interest? Fibers which appear to be resilient when dry may not be when wet. Fibers which recover rapidly after one distortion may not recover after repeated distortions. The scientist therefore makes his tests under an arbitrarily selected combination of conditions and then interprets them according to their presumed relative importance in service.

To show how important this arbitrary selection of test conditions can be, let us consider one example of an incorrect interpretation of test results. One fiber was found to have an excellent elastic recovery after it had been stretched almost to its breaking point. As a matter of fact, in this type of test it was even better than wool. It might be assumed that if this were so, this fiber should provide wrinkle resistance in suits and warmth in blankets. But actually fabrics made with this fiber do not behave that way. Naturally the scientists and engineers searched for the answer to this anomaly. They found that the secret lay in the fact that, although this fiber had good elastic recovery from extreme stretching, it did not recover as well from small extensions and from bending.

In normal use, although there may be rather large distortions in the fabric, rearrangements of fibers in the lofty woolen and worsted structures keep the actual distortion of individual fibers low. Fiber extensions of 5 per cent or less have been indicated as reasonable to represent actual service. Laboratory tests have shown that wool and silk are outstanding in their immediate elastic recovery from distortions in this critical range.

Wool fabrics leave the mills in a slightly stretched condition due to strains induced in the final finishing processes. Before manufacture into garments the fabrics are relaxed by application of moisture and steam followed by drying without tension. With the natural recovery forces relaxed, the fabric is stabilized dimensionally and is "ready for the needle."

When the completed garment is given its final fitting to the wearer, there will be local areas which require minute adjustment for the perfect fit. The human form is so complicated that it defies even the greatest skill with scissors and needle alone. Here the natural plasticity of wool is employed as the final step for perfection. We have all seen the fitter mark a new suit with chalk around the shoulders and across the back. These are signals for the presser to shrink the fabric a bit here, and stretch it a little there. The garment is then manipulated under steam to conform to the desired contours and these contours are then "set" by drying. The garment has been molded to the individual.

In addition to the felting advantages of wool in obtaining fit, the tailors and garment makers like wool for other reasons. Wool's heat resistance means that normal sewing speeds can be maintained without fear of melting the fabric from heat generated by the friction of the needles. Wool's plasticity when moist allows the tailor to press out old creases in alterations and to insert new creases at will. Wool fabrics seldom ravel and edges require no special attention with French seams and binding to avoid dangling threads. Wool seams present no special problem in seam slippage.

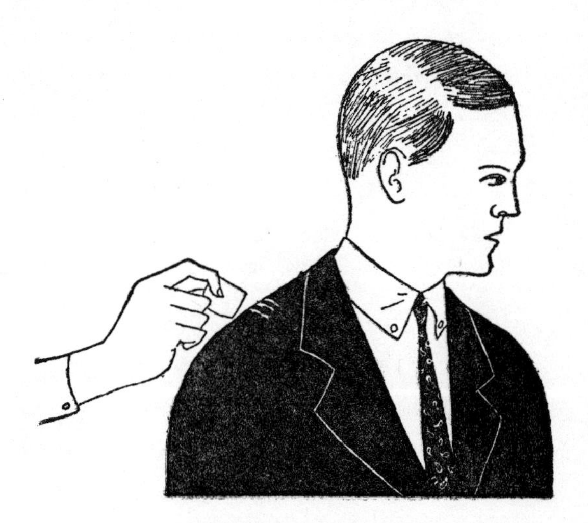

"We have all seen the fitter mark a new suit with chalk around the shoulders and across the back."

And so we see that wool's inherent extensibility, its resilience, its softness and pliability, its moisture absorption, its moist plasticity, and its heat resistance all work together to provide the much desired fit, shape retention, and tailoring qualities required in superior apparel fabrics.

Wrinkle Resistance

The wrinkle resistance of woolen and worsted garments is well known. As a matter of fact, when early attempts were made to manufacture summer suits from substitute fibers, one of the difficult problems encountered was how to develop a fabric which would not, after a few hours' wear, look as though it had been slept in. (Of course, one approach was to design the seersuckers which looked as though they had been slept in before they were worn at all.)

The chemists were called in to develop special treatments to give those fibers, which normally have little or no resilience, a sort of chemical crutch to assist in reducing wrinkling and mussing. Although the chemists worked assiduously at the task and the physicists were called in to evaluate the treatments, it was not until the public had purchased the fabrics and subjected them to actual service conditions that the value of the treatments was proved or disproved.

But chemical finishes have disadvantages which cause confusion to the consumer, frustration to the dry cleaner, and lawsuits for both. It appears that some types of stains will actually unite with the chemicals applied and the stain cannot be removed without removing the treatment itself. As a matter of fact, wrinkle-resistant treatments can be overdone. If too much foreign material is used, the stresses of service are concentrated and wear resistance is radically reduced.

So much has been written and advertised about the

"wrinkle-resistant" properties of chemically treated fabrics that the consumer is inclined to forget the natural wrinkle resistance of wool. This property is so natural to wool that it is taken as a matter of course. People sometimes become confused by advertisements and even inquire for wrinkle-resistant treatments for wool. They are apparently unaware that such finishes were developed to imitate one of wool's intrinsic qualities.

The wrinkle resistance of wool comes from its natural resilience which is discussed more completely under *Fit, Shape Retention and Tailoring.* Wool has an extremely high immediate elastic recovery which keeps fabrics fresh looking and relatively wrinkle free. But wool has still another asset. It has a delayed recovery which provides almost complete removal of even deeply embedded wrinkles if a time interval is allowed. That is the reason that if wrinkles develop in a suit or dress, after a long automobile trip in humid weather, they will hang out over night. Wool's wrinkle resistance is so outstanding that wool is frequently incorporated in blends of cheaper fibers, in lieu of chemical treatments.

It is also significant that wool fiber is resilient both when wet and when dry. All other absorbent fibers lose some of their resilience when wet. If a wrinkle or crease is set in the fiber while wet and allowed to dry while held in a distorted position, the crease will be maintained until the fiber is again moistened. This is the principle used in pressing the crease in trousers. When undesirable creases have been set in the fabric, it is only necessary to remoisten the fabric and the natural recovery forces of the wool fiber will bring it back to its original form. This is why wool products are pressed under a dampened cloth.

Crushing and mussing under humid conditions can, of course, be eliminated by the use of nonabsorbent fibers. Wrinkle resistance is thus improved at the expense of those desirable fabric qualities which depend on absorption. In addition, the use of nonabsorbent fibers introduces new disadvantages: wicking and static. Wicking is discussed in connection with rain repellence where it is most important. Static can cause considerable inconvenience in apparel. It can cause trousers or skirts to cling in an ugly manner and it attracts soil and lint.

(a) wool skirt (b) static charged skirt

"Static . . . can cause trousers or skirts to cling in an ugly manner. . . ."

Absorbent fibers do not present serious problems from static because the moisture they attract from the surrounding air assists greatly in preventing the accumulation of strong electrical potentials.

Here again the importance of the proper balance of properties is emphasized. Wool, being both resilient and absorptive, provides wrinkle resistance without serious problems of wicking and static.

Color and Dyeing

Unless we wish to use a fiber in its natural color it must be dyed. Science has developed numerous chemicals which will impart to the fiber the whole spectrum of colors in varying degrees of brightness and intensity. But dyes are like people and have personalities of their own involving whole patterns of characteristics. They must be selected for their permanence, the way they withstand sunlight, the deleterious acids in the air, sea water, washing, dry cleaning, pleating, perspiration, and cosmetics.

Dyestuffs vary in their ability to withstand these influences. They may be highly resistant to one exposure and weak in others. Some dyestuffs which produce the most brilliant shades may lack one or another of these fastness qualities, while dyes which give almost unlimited fastness toward sunlight may not provide the most satisfactory washing fastness. A dyestuff might be ideal for a delicate pastel shade in a woman's dress and be perfectly satisfactory in fastness for a season or two, but it might be quite unsatisfactory in a man's suit which must stand years of dry cleaning and exposure to the weather and sunlight. The textile manufacturer must pick and choose his dyes with an eye to the particular type of service involved. The selection of the proper balance of desirable qualities in a dyestuff for a given type of service requires careful attention by the manufacturer.

But there is another limitation to be considered. The dyestuff must be such that it can be attached to the fiber with a minimum of difficulty. Dyes are attached to fibers mechanically, chemically, and through a combination of the two. When chemical union can be obtained between the dye and the fiber itself the job is made easy. In other cases, combining chemicals called mordants are used. Mordants have an affinity for both the fiber and some dyestuffs and serve to hold together chemically a dyestuff and a fiber which otherwise have no natural affinity. If there are no chemical means of anchoring the color, it must be attached mechanically. The availability of means for attaching the dyestuff is therefore an important additional consideration beyond the characteristics of hue, brilliance, intensity, and many types of fastness, and sometimes places severe limitation on the manufacturer's selection.

In order to obtain a chemical union between the dyestuff and a fiber, there must be some kind of a chemical hook in the structure of the fiber to fit a matching chemical handle on the dyestuff. These chemical hooks are really unsatisfied chemical appetites which are seeking fulfillment. In some cases they may have found partial satisfaction by joining together with other supplementary groups in the fiber itself, forming temporary alliances which may be readily broken to form a stronger attachment if such is presented by a dyestuff.

Most dyestuffs have, or may be developed with, an active unsatisfied chemical group looking for a chemical partner. The type of active group, or "hook" if you will, which can be built into any particular dyestuff is limited by the overall chemistry of that dyestuff. After all, we have stretched the ingenuity of the dyestuff manufacturer already to provide the colors, hues, intensities, and various types of fastnesses demanded by a public whose

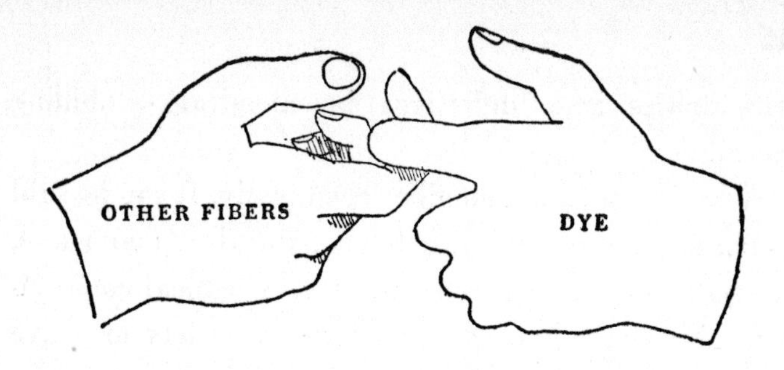

"(Some) fibers have only one type of chemically active constituents in their make-up."

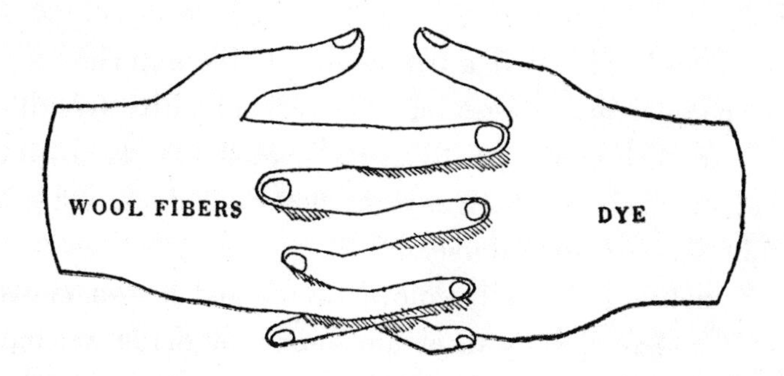

"(Wool's) chemical structure includes a variety of active chemical groups which are ready and anxious to unite with other chemicals."

requirements are increasing as the variety of their occupations and pastimes widens.

Some fibers have no chemical activity and chemical bonds cannot be relied upon to attach coloring matter to the fibers. Other fibers have only one type of chemically active constituents in their make-up. Few fibers present to the dyer a sufficient range of active chemical groups to allow much choice in selecting dyestuffs to give the ideal balance of color and fastness with their associated peculiarities and limitations in chemical combining power.

Wool is a very unique fiber chemically. It can be said that it is the most complex fiber, natural or man-made, in its internal construction and in its chemical composition. Its chemical structure includes a variety of active chemical groups which are ready and anxious to unite with other chemicals. It can combine with an alkaline material or with an acidic material. Protein fibers, such as wool and silk, have the greatest variety of chemically active constituents of all the fibers. These constituents can be utilized to give a tremendous latitude in choosing dye compounds because the fiber can unite directly with so many different types of dyes. Wool can be dyed with acid or basic colors, chromes, metalized dyes, indigo, and to some extent vat dyes.

Sometimes naturally colored black and brown wools are blended directly to obtain a desired shade without dyeing, or shaded with a minimum of dyestuff to shift the natural color to a desired match. It is apparent that dyeing can be used only to secure a darker color than the undyed material. Much wool coming from the sheep's back (after scouring or washing) is an off-white which can be dyed to most of the commercial shades. When extreme clarity is desired, or very light shades are in demand, wools can be found which are sufficiently white. Hence, there are no limitations involved in the basic color of the fiber and, although wool can be bleached to enable the economical use of the darker wools, a considerable proportion of normal unbleached fibers is available for the light and pastel shades.

Soil Resistance

There are two distinct effects to be considered in connection with soil. The first is the relative tendency of the fabric to attract and retain soil. The second is the extent to which soil shows on the fabric.

The two principal types of soil are solid particles which may adhere to the surface of the fabric, and soluble materials which may be dried onto the fabric after spillage. The solid particles may be attached to the fabric by direct contact, by deposition from the air, or they may be suspended in a liquid and left on the fabric when it dries. This last case will be discussed under liquid soiling.

The cross section of the wool fiber has a more or less smooth outline. It is more difficult for soil to cling to such a fiber than to one with an indented cross section which would tend to trap minute particles.

We have also emphasized that the wool fiber is very flexible. In use the fibers are constantly being stretched, bent, twisted, and then allowed to recover. This working of the fibers is frequently effective in dislodging surface deposits of solid particles. Furthermore, many wool structures present a hairy surface. Soil particles are caught on the very outer surface of the fabric before they can become embedded in the yarns. Further movement of the fabric, coupled with the springy nature of the fibers, serves to snap off such superficially held particles.

Where the normal working of the fabric is insufficient

to dislodge solid particles, a light brushing is extremely effective. In this case the action of the brush is assisted by the resilience or snap of the fibers on the fabric surface.

In addition to these simple mechanical influences, it has been noted before in this discussion that wool has both resilience and high moisture absorption. In contrast, low moisture absorption would allow static accumulation which attracts lint and dirt from the surrounding air, and once the particles are in contact with the fabric they would be held securely. The combination of resilience and high moisture absorption in wool is important in reducing soil accumulation, and making it easier to remove.

Another mechanism is involved in the case of liquid-borne soil. When liquid containing suspended particles, or foreign materials in solution, dries on a fabric, the foreign matter is left in the form of soil. On the other hand, if the liquid is removed before drying the foreign matter is carried away with it.

Liquids are only absorbed slowly in wool fabrics. If liquid is spilled on a slanted surface, it runs off. If spilled on a flat, horizontal wool surface, an appreciable time interval is required before the liquid sinks in. This allows opportunity to mop up the spillage before it dries. The repellence of wool fiber surfaces to liquid water is reflected in our normal reactions without thought of the theory or principle involved. For example, one would never take an old wool sweater to mop up a puddle when a cotton rag is at hand.

Fabrics differ greatly in the way they show stains and spots. Plain or light colors and smooth finishes always show soil more readily than mixed colors, dark colors, or textured surfaces. Wool, of course, can be fabricated into the widest variety of textures. A large number of these textures present a broken surface and even in plain colors soil is not easily discernible. Woolen and worsted fabrics have a decorative richness in appearance that makes it unnecessary to resort exclusively to bright and clear colors to attract the eye. Wool also has natural, rich luster upon which spots and stains are less noticeable than on a fabric which has a high sheen and a smooth, mirror-like surface.

Wool's resilient, hairy surface, its low static and its low liquid absorption, all help to resist soil attachment. Wool's textures and rich luster in fabrics reduce the noticeability of soil.

Cleaning

There is nothing new about soil or its removal. In previous generations soil was more of a problem, to the extent that there was more to be contended with, than it is in our present-day lives. Everyone had to work harder physically and this greater activity meant more perspiration with its dried products to be removed. In addition, they bathed less frequently and to a certain extent the skin was cleansed by friction against the underclothing.

Even as late as a generation ago, people were brought into more frequent and intimate contact with foreign materials which soiled their clothes and themselves. The chores around a farm (the great movement from the farm to the city is of comparatively recent origin) involved constant contact with soil producing materials. In the cities, fireplaces, stoves, and furnaces required regular handling of both fuel and its ash. In countless ways individuals in all walks of life encountered dirt and undoubtedly picked up an appreciable amount of it.

The history of laundering seems to extend as far back into unrecorded history as that of the sheep. Since prehistoric man discarded the hide of the sheepskin he wore and found ways of fashioning the shorn wool into cloth, wool has been washed.

In the oldest times the clothes were pounded with sticks on flat stones by the side of a running stream. Later the laundering process was transferred to the washboard and washtub. Saponin, extracted from various plants such as soapwort and soapbark, was replaced by

"In the oldest times the clothes were pounded with sticks on flat stones by the side of a running stream."

"Later the laundering process was transferred to the washboard and washtub."

soft soap made from waste kitchen fat and wood ashes. Then the wooden tub gave way first to the galvanized iron tub, and later to the soapstone sink.

In all of this development there was one ingredient which remained constant—personal attention. It was no problem, therefore, to give woolen garments enough special attention to avoid serious shrinkage. Furthermore, it was customary for the housewife to allow for a reasonable amount of relaxation shrinkage when purchasing or making both wool and cotton garments.

There were other influences which reduced the laundry problem. With washing done in the home, frequently by the same individual who did the buying, there was a marked preference shown for outerwear in practical colors which did not show soil. The newest garments were reserved for dress-up occasions. Suits and coats were not customarily washed and spots were removed by local treatment. Infrequently a pair of trousers or a dress was tubbed. Otherwise, with careful use confined to relatively clean leisure activities, intervals for airing between wearings, and the common use of long-sleeved and long-legged underwear, soil was a minor problem in outerwear until the garment had been reduced to everyday or work use when it mattered less. The natural soil-resisting qualities of wool, as outlined in the preceding chapter, played a very important part in making all this possible.

Meanwhile the long-handled underwear and wool socks were washed as regularly as Monday morning came around. Scarves, sweaters, blankets, and shawls were laundered periodically. Had there been any serious desire to wash suits and coats, they would have been developed fashionwise in quite different designs—without padding, linings, and trim which preclude successful washing regardless of the fiber content of the principal fabric.

Modern life has introduced entirely new problems of cleaning. Instead of dressing up only for Sundays, the greater portion of our people are engaged in daily activities which require more formal attire. Although these activities do not involve the soil risks of farm life, the soot in cities introduces its own problem. Wider travel has broadened our tastes and even the practical New Englander has come to associate with every month of the year the brilliant colors of summer and the tropics.

Lightweight suitings have come into use in summer and the lightweight topcoats between seasons. Both the new fabric textures and changing tastes in colors have had their effect in the greater employment of light colors. Fashions are no longer considered regional. The more constant use of the tailored suit, dresses and coats, which involves more frequent purchases, encourages the consumer to select patterns and colors that would never be considered in a garment expected to last for many years. The startling, the novel, and the extremely light colors, all fit into this new pattern.

In the meantime, there have been parallel improvements to keep pace with the demands of the times. Dry cleaning was developed and became inexpensive enough to be adopted as a regular maintenance routine. The service was made easily available with wide distributions of cleaning plants and multiples of this distribution in pick-up and delivery facilities.

The dry cleaning techniques were first applied to woolen, worsted and silk fabrics and have extended to all fabrics which might demand extra care in washing. In effect, the public transferred its cleaning problems requiring specialized attention from the wash tubs to the shoulders of the dry cleaner.

The cleaner has not been altogether happy with the complications presented by new fibers, and fabrics made of blends of two or three, or even four fibers, each one

"Dry cleaning was developed and became inexpensive enough to be adopted as a regular maintenance routine."

different from the other in basic properties, and many of them antagonistic to the proper treatment of the others. When he received an all-wool garment he knew exactly what to do. Dry cleaners have well established standard methods for processing wool, including removal of water soluble soils. Today he is burdened with a whole new catalog of problems.

He is receiving not only many new fibers but blends of these fibers further complicated by chemical finishes. Each fiber and each finish requires its own method of treatment and precautions. They have their varied melting or softening points which must be avoided in pressing. They have reactions to solvents and spotting chemicals. Soils may unite with certain finishes and cannot be removed without taking the finish with them. Some finishes even disappear entirely, leaving a fabric that can hardly be identified with the original. The cleaner must either identify or guess at the constituents of each garment. If he guesses wrong the results are unsatisfactory and his customer is unhappy.

In these newly developing dry cleaning problems the public is caught in the middle. It is impossible for the consumer to know the properties of each of the new fibers, let alone to be familiar with the various blends of them. The retail sales people are as confused as the public. Even when cleaning instructions are available at the time of purchase, they are seldom at hand when the time for cleaning arrives. With the ever widening combinations of fibers, the consumer is lucky to remember which fibers are included in which garment. The cleaner is completely in the dark because the new fibers imitate

"The cleaner must either identify or guess at the constituents of each garment."

"When he received an all-wool garment he knew exactly what to do."

the finish, appearance, and sometimes the long established, descriptive names of fabrics made of the traditional natural fibers, wool, silk and cotton.

Since dry cleaning is today almost the universal method of cleaning apparel which requires special care, both home and commercial laundering have been reduced to assembly line methods. Even drying is automatic, and personal attention is not required until the material is ready to be ironed.

The washing of those utility woolen articles which require frequent launderings has been made much more convenient than in the days when woolies were tubbed regularly as part of the family wash. Shrink-control treatments have been developed to a point where the army can specify and obtain shrink-resisting wool garments which will stand even the severe felting action of the

". . . both home and commercial laundering have been reduced to assembly line methods . . . and personal attention is not required until the material is ready to be ironed."

mobile army laundry. Civilian shrink-resisting socks, sweaters and shirts are available, with no change in texture, for hand washing without resort to boarding and the extra care used in previous generations. With little change in hand, treatments can be applied for woolens to withstand even controlled mechanical washing as has been demonstrated by the army in mass practice.

It would seem evident from all this that dry cleaning and shrink-control treatments have eliminated any serious problems of wool cleaning. Much of today's advertising of fabrics raises washability to such a position of importance that it supersedes more important qualities. Among these are wool's absorbency which is so necessary to warmth, hand, reduction of static, prevention of chills and prevention of wicking.

Strangely enough, the impression is well rooted that wool can't stand exposure to water. This is absurd. Wool, fresh from the back of the sheep, is and has been for ages past washed in streams in primitive countries just as clothes are washed there by beating with sticks. When wool enters the mill the first process to which it is subjected is a soap and water wash, called scouring. Wool is boiled for hours in water solutions of dye to give it color. In yarns and piece goods, oil is washed out with soap and water. Wool is milled and fulled in soap and water, and steamed in the final finishing and repeatedly thereafter during garment making and pressing.

Durability

Wear Resistance

The scientists have defined wear resistance as the ability to absorb energy and to give it back without being destroyed in the process. The flexibility of wool yarns allows them to cooperate in distributing wear among many individual fibers. Furthermore, wool fibers are tough. They can be bent back on themselves more than 20,000 times without being broken. This is compared with the rupture of Sea Island cotton after 3,200 bends, natural silk after 1,800, and viscose rayon after 75.

There are many fibers which are stronger than wool. However, fiber strength is not a direct indication of wear resistance because the construction of the fabric and the ability of the fibers to distribute loads eliminates the demand for extreme fiber strength.

Wear, as we understand it in general service, does not necessarily mean creation of holes. As soon as the fabric begins to show a change in its surface appearance, its value depreciates and, if the change is severe, we are forced to discard it.

An individual fiber can be too strong. While a fabric is worn, short ends are loosened from the surface of the yarns. The number of fibers dislodged is usually small compared with the total and there is no damage as long as they drop off or can be removed readily by brushing. When fibers of great strength are present, little balls of fuzz may accumulate on the surface of the fabric and they can be held fast by individual strong fibers which have one end caught into the yarn structure. This phenomenon is called pilling. Some of the extremely strong fibers are known to develop pills after very little wear.

When the pills are small, a dusty irregular appearance is first noted. As the pills increase in size the fabric surface becomes very rough and irregular. Naturally this seriously interferes with the practical serviceability of a fabric even though no holes are worn through and no yarns are broken. A fabric can be strong enough to support a very heavy weight and still be so objectionable in its appearance as to be useless in apparel.

On very rare occasions, as for example in soft sweaters or loose weave suitings made from short fibers in low twist yarns, even wool has been known to pill in places where the rubbing is excessive. However, this is the exception found only in extremes of construction. In most fabrics wool is free from pilling.

Tear Resistance

Tear resistance has an important influence on the length of service in lightweight fabrics—especially those which may be worn during more vigorous activities. A common type of tear is the three-cornered tear, but all tears result from a strong force applied locally as when a fabric catches on a nail.

Tear resistance is obtained in a window screen by the use of very strong wires, so strong that, when an outside force is applied at any one point, the wires at that point

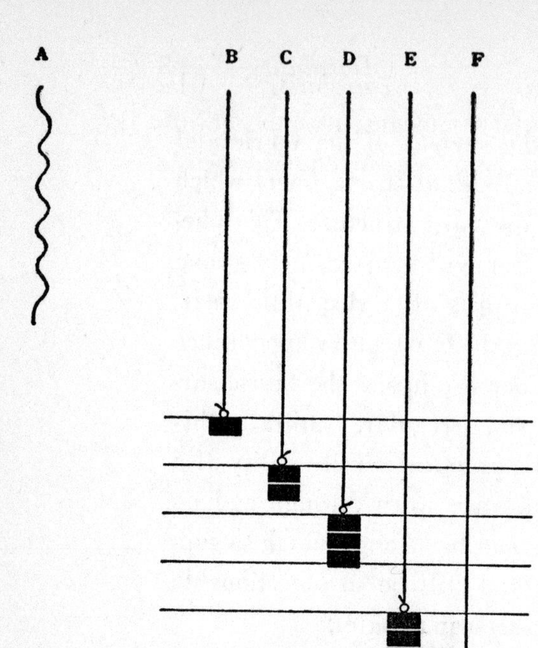

A) crimped wool fiber. B, C, D, E, F) fiber loaded with one, two, three, four and five units of weight.

". . . crimp is removed easily, but the next extensions . . . require considerable force. . . . When distortion has exceeded approximately 5 per cent, the fiber protects itself by extending with little resistance . . ."

are strong enough to resist all of the force exerted on them. But who wants to wear a garment made of metallic screening.

In textiles, tear resistance depends upon the distribution of destructive forces so that many individual fibers are brought into play. This ingenious principle makes it possible to obtain softness, pliability, and hand, along with sufficient tear resistance for normal exposures.

The properties required in the individual elements for the proper distribution of loads are flexibility, toughness, and elasticity. Toughness means here the ability to absorb energy without being destroyed. Meanwhile the construction in which these elements are placed must be so designed as to allow these properties to be utilized. It would be useless to employ a flexible element to distribute loads in a design which would not allow the movement required. This is the reason that a heavy application of a chemical finish can decrease wear and tear resistance because it makes the fabric too unyielding. In clothing, great flexibility is demanded for comfort and a large amount of temporary distortion of the fabric is allowable as long as the fabric will spring back to its original shape.

When a tearing force is exerted on a fabric made of wool, the fibers at first extend themselves very easily as they uncrimp. As we previously noted, the crimp is removed easily, but the next extensions or bending require considerable force. Wool is stiffest in the distortions just following the removal of crimp. It is then that the fibers put up the greatest "fight," absorbing the energy which might otherwise cause rupture. Finally when distortion has exceeded approximately 5 per cent, the fiber protects itself by extending with little resistance all the way up to 30 per cent of its original length without breaking.

Meanwhile, thousands of additional fibers have been brought into play. Each has made its initial easy distortion to get into the best possible position to minimize its abuse and has exerted its maximum resistance and energy absorption until it has been distorted to the point where it extends with comparative ease to distribute the load further, in effect "calling up reinforcements." It can be seen that through this marvelous system the extensibility of wool fibers contributes much to wool's tear resistance.

We have also indicated that wool fibers tend to repel each other, and even in high-twist worsteds, which bind the fibers closely together, they take up the maximum space permitted in the construction specification. For that reason, the way in which wool fibers lie in a given construction assures a maximum opportunity for the individual fibers to squirm around within the yarns in order to distribute the load with a minimum of strain on each fiber.

Finally, after the tearing force is removed, the natural elasticity of wool makes each fiber spring back into place. This in turn forces the yarns and fabric back into their original position and shape.

Weathering Resistance

Because wool is warm and contributes so much to style and texture interest while maintaining a well groomed appearance through shape retention and soil resistance, wool is most frequently worn as an outer covering where it is exposed to sunlight, occasional rain or "weather." Wool is chemically active and this characteristic is responsible for the wide choice of dyestuffs from which the dyer can select just the type of fastness he desires for the service involved. Wool, in other words, cooperates with the dyer in making it easy to apply fast colors which will withstand extended exposure to weathering.

Meanwhile, the fiber itself will withstand extensive exposure as required in normal garment wear. This is especially exhibited in men's suits and overcoats as there is hardly a family that does not include at least one man who boasts of a suit or a coat which has been worn ten years or more and is still in good condition.

Perspiration Resistance

Perspiration, too, is frequently mentioned as a chemical hazard. However, analysis of consumer complaints indicates that the perspiration hazard is more concerned with color than fiber damage. Here again the wide range of dyes, which will attach themselves chemically to wool, gives wool a tremendous advantage in assisting the dyer to provide perspiration-fast colors for wool.

Moth Resistance

Insects are noted for their ability to adapt themselves to live on the materials at hand. In some cases they have even adjusted to drugs made expressly to annihilate them. It is natural that wool is subject to moth damage, particularly if greasy soil is present.

Years of experience in handling woolens have produced simple methods for protection. Clothes which are used frequently are seldom attacked if they are kept clean. Housewives have learned to store their garments sealed from marauding insects. Sealing is a good idea anyway as it protects from dust and soil. Paradichlorbenzene placed in an airtight storage container (3 ounces per 5 cubic feet); DDT sprays; active immersion of 0.5% DDT solution; or application of EQ–53, the emulsifiable DDT for use in connection with washing or rinsing, all give good protection.

Moth resistance may be obtained also from a number of products which are applied during dry cleaning and are convenient to use just prior to storage. Such treatments must be renewed with each cleaning. Many dry cleaners apply them as a matter of routine and practically all cleaners will do so on request.

Fabrics can also be purchased treated to provide satisfactorily durable protection even after dry cleaning or laundering. Many specialty fibers such as vicuna, camels hair, and cashmere, which are particularly subject to moth attack, are mothproofed by the manufacturer without any specific mention of it. As such specialty fibers are sold with special emphasis on their luxurious "hand," it can be seen that moth resistance can be accomplished without damage to the texture.

Warmth

Essentially wool is warm because it has both resilience and high moisture absorption capacity. Both properties are required in civilian fabrics to maintain body comfort. There have been instances where simple insulation has been provided without absorption and such fabrics will show good insulation tests as long as the fabric is dry. However, such tests ignore basic conditions of garment wear.

Special arctic garments have been designed for military purposes without the use of absorbent fibers, but these garments must protect the individual under such extreme climatic conditions that fit, appearance, flexibility, and other factors which we consider vital to civilian life must be ignored. In these military garments body moisture is taken care of through mechanisms which are quite incompatible with civilian demands.

We are therefore justified in the statement that, for civilian use, if either resilience or high moisture absorption capacity is lacking, a fabric cannot protect the wearer from the cold. Wool has both properties.

The insulation value of a fabric depends on the air entrapped within it and on its surface. The actual conductivity of the fibers themselves is not important as the largest part of the total volume of most fabrics is air and the conductivity of the entrapped air is the limiting influence. In woolen and worsted fabrics, which are lofty and porous because wool fibers repel each other, roughly 80 per cent of the total fabric volume is made up of air.

"Essentially wool is warm because it has both resilience and high moisture absorption capacity."

Air, of course, is a very poor conductor of heat and the higher the percentage of air in the volume of a fabric the greater the insulation value.

Because practically all apparel fabrics contain large amounts of air the simple insulation value of a fabric is approximately proportional to its thickness. It is relatively easy to make a fabric which is thick but it is a little more difficult to make a fabric that is both thick and light. It is still more difficult to make a fabric that maintains its thickness and lightness in actual use which, of course, involves repeated crushing, folding, and distortions. Only resilient fibers will maintain their thickness with light weight, and wool is among the most resilient of all fibers under service conditions.

Another influence on the insulation value of a fabric is the degree to which the fibers are uniformly separated within the yarns and within the fabric. One could make a fabric with dense yarns leaving large open spaces between the yarns but such fabrics would be poor insulators when there is movement of air. The open spaces would create channels through which the air could pass taking heat from the body quickly.

On the other hand, one could develop a thick dense fabric in which each fiber presses closely against its

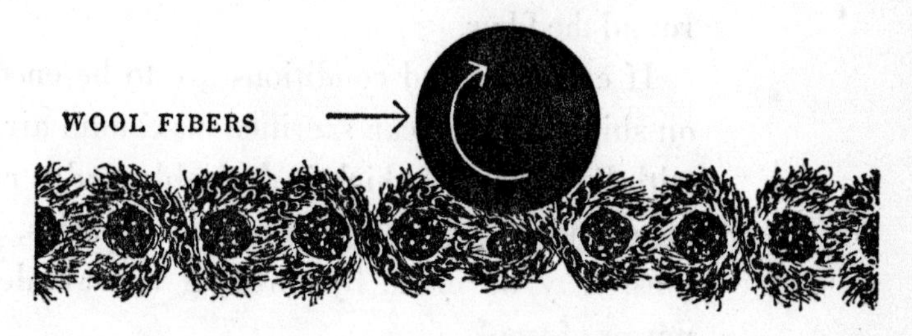

"Only resilient fibers will maintain their thickness with light weight, and wool is among the most resilient of all fibers under service conditions."

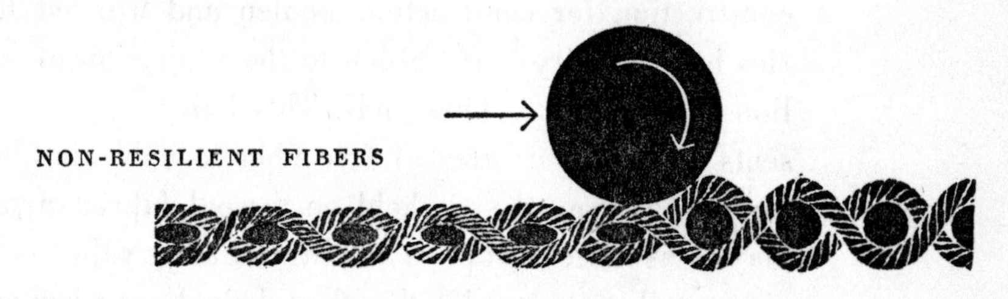

neighbor. Such a fabric would be stiff and heavy, and the lack of entrapped air would mean that heat would be conducted through the fibers rather than through the still air held by the fibers.

The natural fiber-to-fiber repellence of wool, which we observed when we first considered the wool fiber, assures the most uniform distribution of fibers and the greatest amount of free fiber area within the yarns and fabric. Furthermore, the resilience of wool enables the fibers to maintain such a distribution during the fabric distortions of actual service.

The concept that air is held in fabrics in separated

compartments or individual walled cells is erroneous. Air is actually held closely and tenaciously against the fiber surfaces. In high velocity air movement this film is somewhat reduced, but as long as the fiber is free for contact with the air a perceptible film of air will surround the fiber.

If extreme wind conditions are to be encountered, as on shipboard, we can sacrifice maximum air entrapment with light weight which is desirable under more normal air conditions. Dense wind-resistant fabrics, such as meltons, may be made by utilizing the wonderful felting power of wool.

Just as air is entrapped within the fabric, air is also held close to the fabric surface. We have mentioned that construction for construction woolen and worsted fabrics have a hairy surface due to the projection of millions of individual fiber ends. This hairy surface presents an enormous area of free fiber to hold air films. For this reason, the air held on a wool fabric surface may be as large in volume and in insulating value as the air actually entrapped within the fabric. Even when wet, wool does not lose its resilience. The hairy surface is maintained and with it the insulating film of still air.

The thickness and effectiveness of this surface layer of air can be increased by creating a dense outer fur of projecting ends. For that reason we raise a high nap on blankets by teasing individual fiber tips out from the surface yarns.

Air trapped between layers of clothing also provides an important barrier to heat loss from the body. Wool clothing does not develop high static charges which would cause the fabric to cling tightly to skin surfaces or to adjacent layers of clothing. The resilience of the surface fibers of wool, which is maintained even in the presence of body moisture, discourages close skin-to-wool-fabric contact, while the absorbed moisture discourages the accumulation of static charges. Hence, the air entrapment between layers of clothing and next to the skin is controlled by fit and design and is not eliminated by static.

The surface character of woolen and worsted fabrics is responsible in an important way for its reputation for being warm to the touch. In addition to the fact that wool absorbs moisture, the hairy surface of fabrics made from wool presents a very small area of actual contact with the skin. When we touch a surface, the first instantaneous reaction of coolness or warmth depends on whether the surface is at a higher or lower temperature than the skin. Most fabrics are at a lower temperature than our skin, and heat will pass from our skin to the fabric until the contacting surface has been brought up to skin temperature.

If a fabric surface is slick and smooth there is a considerable area of fabric to be warmed before the temperatures are the same. Fibers which pack in yarns and in fabrics give this slick smooth surface and hence feel cool to the touch. However in the case of wool, the skin contacts only tiny sections or ends of fibers. The actual area contacted is extremely low and the volume of fiber to be heated is minute indeed. For that reason the areas contacted are heated so rapidly that there is practically no sensation of heat loss and a woolen fabric feels warm. Worsted fabrics, having less hairiness, present a smoother surface and hence feel somewhat cooler than woolens. That is the reason that worsted fabrics are used in summer as will be discussed later.

"Worsted fabrics, having less hairiness, present a smoother surface and hence feel somewhat cooler than woolens."

The body exudes moisture even when cold. This moisture must be removed or it will carry heat away from the body at 20 times the rate of the air it replaces. The uniform distribution of the wool fibers in fabric structures allows for a maximum diffusion of water vapor outward for a specified porosity or wind resistance. In addition, water vapor which does not pass through the fabric is readily absorbed. The absorbed moisture is, of course, unavailable for evaporation and consequent cooling. Wool has the highest absorption capacity of all apparel fibers. It can hold as much as 30 per cent of its weight in moisture without feeling damp.

As wool absorbs moisture it actually creates heat. This phenomenon is called by the scientists "heat of absorption." If you go from the dry atmosphere of a heated room to the moist atmosphere of a cold, damp day, your wool clothes slowly absorb water vapor at the same time generating heat. Under these conditions, a heavy wool overcoat can generate as much heat as the human body does in two or three hours. This phenomenon is the partial basis of claims that wool has thermostatic properties.

It has been suggested that nonabsorbent fibers will dispose of body moisture by wicking. Wicking is the power to suck water along the fibers or between them just as a lamp wick sucks up oil. It should be noted that wicking does not take place until water vapor has accumulated and condensed as liquid water. Hence, the fabric is well saturated when moisture is transmitted to the outer surface. The water-saturated fabric is a high heat conductor. It is not by accident that we think of a wet fabric as a cold fabric, although we do not usually bother to analyze why this is true.

Furthermore, the liquid water must leave the outer surface by evaporation. Evaporation takes up enormous quantities of heat from this surface thus reducing the outer surface temperature. If the temperature of the outer surface is reduced, the heat transfer through the already highly conductive wet fabric is still further increased as heat conductivity is directly proportional to the temperature difference between the two surfaces.

The high absorption capacity of wool acts three ways to increase warmth. 1. It removes water which would accumulate in a fabric made from nonabsorbent fibers. 2. With such water removed, it is not available to travel through the fabric for evaporation on the outer surface which would further increase the rate of heat loss. 3. In the process of absorbing moisture, wool actually creates heat.

Water absorption also acts to prevent sudden chills. When an individual ceases violent activity or goes from a warm to a cool exposure, sweating stops because the body no longer requires its cooling action. What happens in the initial period after the cessation of activity is especially critical in preventing chills.

When we are overheated and sweating to cool the skin, blood is circulated freely just under the skin exactly as

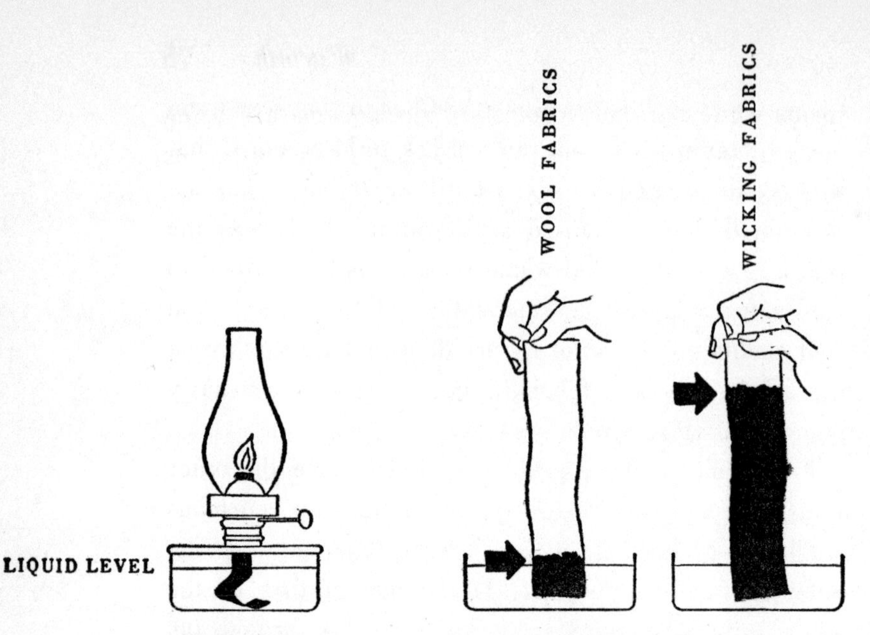

"Wicking is the power to suck water along the fibers or between them just as a lamp wick sucks up oil."

an automobile thermostat directs the flow of hot water to the radiator when the engine is hot. Circulation of the blood under skin areas which are cooled by surface evaporation keeps the internal organs from overheating. When the activity which causes overheating has ceased, or when one passes quickly from a hot to a cold environment, it takes several minutes for the body mechanism to cut off this surface blood circulation and transfer it to the vital organs to help maintain the required internal temperature. Therefore, the very rapid evaporation cooling is particularly serious during the first few minutes while the body is adjusting to new conditions.

With nonabsorptive materials, the water retained on the fabric and fiber surfaces will evaporate rapidly just when it does the most harm. With wool, the absorbed water can evaporate only as it is desorbed and only a very small amount will be desorbed during that first few moments while the body protection mechanisms are being reorganized. Later, after the body makes its adjustments to the new conditions, the blood is withdrawn from the skin surface and the contracted tissues serve as additional insulation while desorbed water is evaporated slowly.

Many laboratories make superficial tests of fabrics and report "warmth" or insulation value. Strictly speaking, most of the tests measure insulation value alone, and under conditions which do not represent actual exposure on the human body.

The simplest test, and unfortunately the most frequently used, merely measures the heat transfer from a warm surface in contact with the fabric. Motion of air over the outer surface is not considered or allowed for. The ability of the fabric to maintain warmth in actual service, or even to maintain thickness or bulk under service conditions, is not considered. Furthermore, these tests are usually run with the fabrics held tightly against the warm surface eliminating the effect of porosity.

Such tests are of little value beyond that obtainable by the mere measurement of thickness at the time of manufacture. Indeed, technical reports have shown that heat transmission measured this way is directly dependent on thickness alone. More recently, consumer tests are beginning to take air movement into consideration. Such tests not only provide measurement under controlled air movement but the fabric sample is held away from the heating surface as in actual service.

Most important of all, laboratory tests are run too frequently with the fabric in a dry or a "conditioned" state. That means that some constant low moisture value is maintained. In actual use on the human body this is far from the case. As we have indicated above, the body is constantly creating moisture, and under some conditions moisture enters from the outside. The way the fiber disposes of this moisture has a most important effect on warmth, and hence a test method which does not allow for this effect may be exceedingly misleading.

Because there are so many inadequate test methods used in reporting "warmth," claims for warmth in a fabric or garment should be carefully checked for their validity under actual service conditions.

Wool in Warm Weather

Under some conditions wool garments may actually become an active agent in protecting the body from outside heat. In the desert, with dry air at temperatures above 100° F and direct exposure to heat radiation from the sun and the sand, a thick wool garment can form a much needed insulating barrier around the body. Furthermore, the small quantity of extremely dry air inside the clothing has a tremendous capacity for evaporating water. Perspiration is evaporated cooling both the skin and the entrapped air next to it. This air is kept cool by the protective sheath of wool in the outer garments. The Arabs make use of this principle with the further advantage that the same heavy garments will protect them from the cold that comes on the desert at night.

Wool is not always worn in climates where its potential warmth is important. It may be worn in the summer time when the wearer might prefer to wear little or no clothes if comfort alone is to be considered.

In most urban communities the direct radiation from the sun is less serious. Air temperatures are usually somewhat below body temperature. Furthermore the air is humid. Because the humid air has little capacity for taking up additional water, free access of the body to a maximum amount of air is most important.

The problem, therefore, is to maintain the accepted standards of appearance with a maximum of comfort. The clothing is selected in urban areas not as an active protection from the heat but to maintain propriety with minimum interference with the body's own cooling mechanisms.

Here again the open, porous character of woolen and, to a lesser extent, worsted fabrics is of tremendous advantage. Opacity and covering power can be maintained in conjunction with a high degree of air transmission. Fibers which pack closely together give impermeable fabrics, or so much space is left between individual yarns that the fabric is transparent.

Beyond the porosity which allows moisture-saturated air to escape from the skin, woolen and worsted fabrics will maintain a fresh, crisp appearance. Wrinkles hang

The Arabs use wool to protect them from the heat of the sun and from the cold of the desert night.

out readily, and the garment maintains its shape and fit in spite of humid weather. It is important to note that this resilience and maintenance of appearance are coupled with absorption, a combination of properties found uniquely in wool. Excess perspiration is absorbed and does not wet the surface of the fabric to drag over the skin uncomfortably. Furthermore, the absorption of perspiration prevents wicking which would create dark unsightly areas on the outer surface.

We have seen that woolen surfaces are especially warm to the touch because they cut down the area of contact with the skin. However, the variety of types of wool fibers allows the manufacturer to design fabrics to minimize this effect at will. The natural hairy characteristic of wool fabrics is reduced radically in worsted constructions.

In making worsted yarns, long fibers are selected and twisted so tightly that they are bound together against their natural tendency to repel each other. Furthermore, as the fibers are long, there is a minimum of unattached fiber ends to extend beyond the fabric surface.

These two influences, the tight twist and the long fibers, in worsted constructions give a smooth surface which is cool to the touch as compared with the rough surface of woolens. Extremely fine worsted yarns can be woven into light, airy, gossamer-like fabrics for women's summer dresses.

Wool's resilience provides light and porous fabrics for warm weather clothing which maintains a crisp fresh appearance. Wool's absorption prevents a damp, clammy touch and its range in fiber length and construction allows for the manufacture of smooth textures with a cool hand.

Rain Repellency

Actually we make rather extreme demands on our clothing, and at times these demands seem to call for contradictory characteristics. For example, we want our garments to assist in the rapid removal of body moisture from the inside, but we want them to discourage admission of water from the outside.

One way to secure the removal of water vapor from the inside would be to use a coarse, open mesh with large areas free for air movement, but such a fabric would not provide suitable covering power. Wool, through its loft or bulking capacity, provides both a maximum porosity and a maximum covering power.

Conversely, the best way to get rain repellence would be to provide a dense impervious sheet, such as that used in the old rubber raincoats. This would give good resistance to rain but no outward transmission of moisture vapor.

Wool manages to give reasonable rain repellence without interfering with body ventilation. This most convenient anomaly is made possible through the influence of three of wool's important properties. They are as follows: a high capacity for water vapor absorption, a natural repellence of the fiber surface for liquid water, and a resilience which provides an ideal fabric surface for shedding water, and which also absorbs the energy of impinging rain.

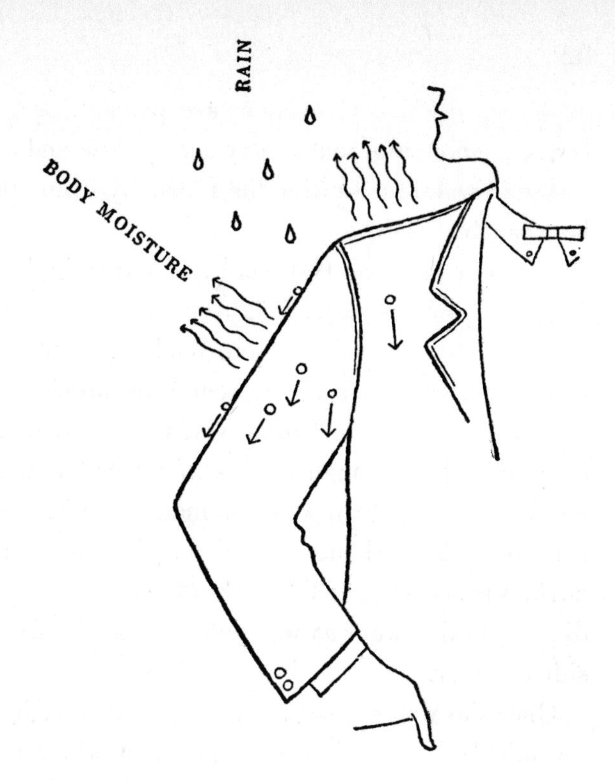

"Wool manages to give a reasonable rain repellence without interfering with body ventilation."

Apparel fibers fall into three general classifications in their behavior toward water: high absorption and low wicking fibers of which wool is an outstanding example; medium absorption and medium wicking fibers such as cotton; and low absorption, high wicking fibers such as the nonabsorptive synthetic fibers. "Wicking" is the property of some fibers to suck liquids (in this discussion, water) along their surfaces, and between the fibers as they lie in yarns and fabrics. "Wicking" may carry liquid through the fabric, from one side to the other, or along the fabric to wet areas not directly exposed by contact or immersion.

Body perspiration may be directly absorbed as water

vapor when absorptive fibers are present, or when the fibers are nonabsorbent it may accumulate and condense as liquid water, saturating the fabric by filling the voids between the fibers.

It has been stated that wool has a very high capacity for absorbing moisture. It is worthwhile to consider the mechanisms of this absorption. We have pointed out that the wool fiber has an outer membrane which is both resistant to chemicals and impervious to water. Water must enter the fiber through breaks in the outer membrane. Even in freshly shorn wool the membrane is broken and usually additional breaks and openings appear during normal processing. If this were not so, it would be most difficult to dye wool as we could not get the dyestuff inside the fiber.

Once the water gets inside the membrane, it is taken up quickly by the interior of the fiber which has a tremendous appetite for moisture. Water vapor can slide through the breaks in the outer skin very easily, while liquid water is actually repelled and seeps through the breaks only with difficulty.

The moisture vapor created by the body is rapidly absorbed in the wool fiber. In contrast the liquid water which contacts the fabric as rain, or as spillage, is repelled by the water-resisting membrane before it enters the fiber.

There is another influence on the preferential absorption of water from the inside rather than the outside. That influence is the physical contour of the fabric surface. Rain reaches the fabric in the form of small, pear-shaped droplets. Actually the rain drops would be spherical in shape except that in falling the sphere is slightly deformed by air friction and gravity.

If these droplets are maintained on the fabric surface, they touch only the fiber tips or small sections of the fibers. The droplets roll away or stand isolated without wetting or penetrating the fabric. Whether the droplet retains its original form or is broken to spread out in a flat, thin sheet depends upon the comparative strengths of two forces.

The first of these forces is the tendency of the outer surface of a liquid to hold together as though this surface were an elastic skin that constantly pulls the free liquid into the smallest possible volume, which is a sphere. The opposing force, working against the former force after the droplet hits the fabric, is the tendency of a solid and a liquid to increase their common contact surface.

In contact with any particular material the tendency for the drop to destroy itself depends importantly on the type of surface involved. If it presents a smooth, flat plane the droplet is much more likely to spread out than if the surface presents a series of individual points which maintain close but separated positions. The feathers of birds and ducks present this type of surface. As a matter of fact, the individual barbs on feathers are so designed that the points are maintained as separate entities. On the other hand, in fur the surface tension of the liquid may draw individual hair tips together so closely that the equivalent of a small flat surface is developed.

The hairy characteristics of many wool fabrics resemble to a large degree the characteristics of the surface of birds' feathers and encourage the maintenance of rain in droplets or pearls. Therefore, in light showers, rain tends to run off without wetting. This is the reason that a Scotch tweed can be worn in a light drizzle or a heavy

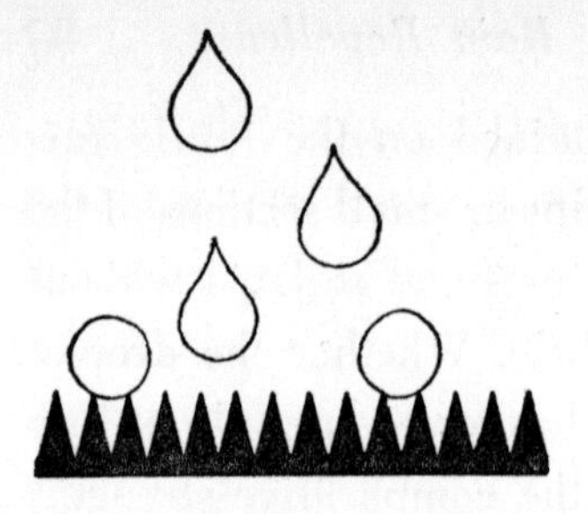
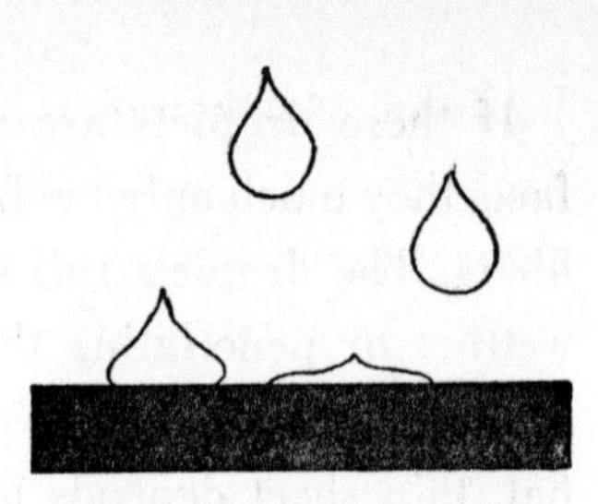

". . . the tendency of the drop to destroy itself depends importantly on the type of surface involved. If it presents a smooth, flat plane the droplet is much more likely to spread out than if the surface presents a series of individual points which maintain close but separated positions."

mist without soaking through. Fibers which cling together to give smooth yarns, or fabrics which present smooth surfaces, encourage the droplets to break and soak in. The natural resilience of wool even when wet assures the maintenance of a hairy surface with resultant rain repellency.

Woolen fabrics also provide rain repellency in another way. Falling drops of rain hit a fabric with an appreciable force. If the surface of the garment is hard and unyielding, all of the energy which has been accumulated in the fall can be utilized in pushing the contents of the drop into the fabric, thus breaking the droplet form. On the other hand, soft compressible fabrics can absorb the energy of a falling droplet, taking up the energy that would otherwise be utilized in assisting the water to penetrate.

Shower tests have shown that an open wool gauze, on which the wool fibers have been lightly felted, is more rain resistant than a waterproofed gabardine. Naturally soft, open structures allow for a maximum of breathing in the fabric, preventing the accumulation of body moisture while resisting the entrance of rain. The rain resistance of even specially waterproofed rainwear is improved if a compressible wool garment is worn underneath.

Flammability

Other things being equal the construction of a fabric has an important effect on its flammability. Burning is a rapid chemical combination of a material with oxygen, usually the oxygen of the air. Therefore, oxygen must be readily available to allow ignition or, once ignited, to encourage the flame to spread to new areas. A dense construction discourages burning because oxygen is less accessible. An illustration of this influence is found with non-fibrous materials. Ordinary flour, when lying undisturbed in a bin, presents little fire hazard but when dispersed in the air in the form of dust, or lying in thin layers on the walls and beams of a loft, the air is so readily available that the flour may burn with explosive violence. In a powdered state even metals such as aluminum will burn violently or explode.

Another influence on flammability and the spread of flame is the effect of the construction on dissipation or retention of heat. Assuming that original ignition is from an outside source, the continuing flame must always seek new material to consume. This new material must be ignited by the heat transmitted from the portion already burning. To a large extent this influence opposes or counteracts the construction influence that provides access to oxygen. A fabric can be so flimsy and so well ventilated that the heat of burning of the small amount of material in any one section is dissipated into the air too fast to ignite new sections. Thus a fabric construction may be too dense to allow for access of oxygen or it may be too flimsy to concentrate enough heat for the spread of flames.

In addition, there is another influence—that of impurities or foreign materials. Such materials as dyes, finishing agents, and textile oils may have chemical or physical effects which assist or depress burning rates and flame propagation.

Because of the somewhat conflicting influences of the above mentioned physical and chemical properties, blends of fibers and new finishes must be given especially careful tests for each new construction and each new blend and finish in that construction, lest the consumer suffer from unpleasant surprises. It is dangerous to predict the performance of a blend from the performance of its individual constituents.

Of particular importance in reducing flammability is the influence of moisture absorption. For example, the insurance laboratories have reported that the moisture absorption of cotton at 80 per cent relative humidity will cut the flame travel through a test strip to nearly half its rate of travel at 35 per cent relative humidity. Wool, of course, absorbs about twice as much moisture as cotton.

Wool can be made to ignite by application of an outside source of flame. After ignition the fiber quickly shrivels away from the flame. Only when the fabric is held so as to heat new fibers constantly and where sufficient oxygen is available in constructions of sufficient density to allow for high heat concentration can the burning be made to continue after removal of the ignition source. In nearly all cases, however, the flame rapidly extinguishes itself, leaving a light ash which immediately cools and can be brushed away. Further-

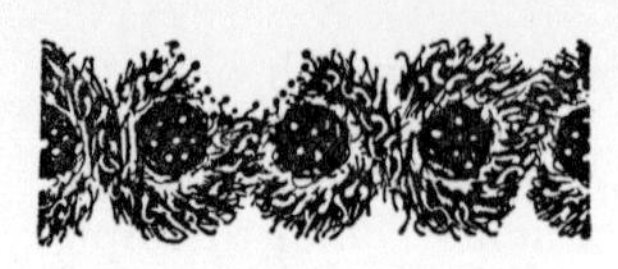

"After ignition (wool) fiber quickly shrivels away from the flame."

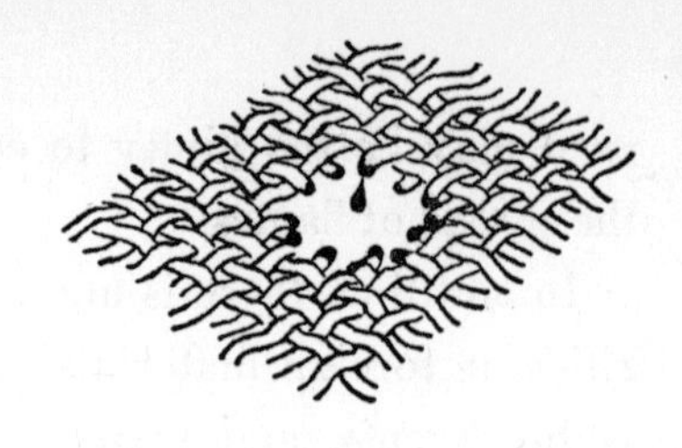

"Melted fibers . . . may be carried to the skin by flowing or dropping or become attached in a momentary contact."

more, burning wool produces a strong characteristic odor which acts as an alarm. We have all experienced cases where the presence of a smoldering cigarette has been made known by the odor of wool in contact with it—a built-in fire alarm.

The characteristics of the residue are important. As a matter of fact it has been recommended that wool should be incorporated with asbestos in suits for fighting oil and gasoline fires. The charred wool insulates the asbestos so that the asbestos can maintain its strength and the fabric its integrity. Here wool is used to improve the effectiveness of even asbestos which is such a well-known fire retardant that it is used in protective fire curtains in theaters.

Wool itself is frequently used as a fire fighting agent. The fire insurance companies recommend the use of wool blankets to smother fires. Almost every laboratory or industrial activity which involves highly inflammable materials requires that wool blankets should be kept readily available to extinguish small fires or ignited clothing.

". . . fire insurance companies recommend the use of wool blankets to smother fires."

Flame itself is not the only hazard involved in burning. Melted fibers can be of even more serious personal hazard than the flame. Flame may be extinguished quickly. Light charred matter can be brushed away without causing serious burns. Melted fibers, however, can stick tenaciously to the flesh, and continue to burn the tissues until ample time is allowed for complete (and slow) cooling. Even if the fiber is not melted in contact with the skin, it may be carried to the skin by flowing or dropping or become attached in a momentary contact.

In discussing fire, we cannot ignore the possibility of the fiber itself creating the original ignition that causes the trouble in the first place. Fibers with high static forming characteristics such as those with low moisture absorption may actually cause sparks which ignite flammable materials in the vicinity.

Blends

This brings us to the very important subject of blends. We have on the market a host of new fibers, some with very different properties which overlap some of the specific properties of wool. More and more these fibers are being blended with wool to supplement their own properties by the broad pattern of properties which only wool can lend to the combination.

In discussing blends we immediately enter the world of fractions, and increase to astronomical figures the already numerous and confusing combinations of constructions and fiber properties with their complex relationships. It might seem at first that this enormous addition to the choices which a manufacturer might make in creating new fabrics would be a tremendous boon to the consumer. On the other hand, like many new tools, they must be used with intelligence. Without a full understanding of their potentialities, for good or evil, and mastery of the techniques for their profitable employment, the market may only become flooded with inferior merchandise which wrecks consumer confidence.

And it must be borne in mind that, once departure is made from the relatively simple standards which have been proved by experience, the consumer and the trade are lost in a flood of unfamiliar labels which are already so numerous that even the garment makers and merchants are confused. Such a condition can only encourage the operation of commercial pressures which penalize, temporarily at least, the more conscientious manufacturers. Even if we have found the perfect blend to give maximum functional and aesthetic results in a specific type of service, these commercial pressures, coupled with the lack of consumer guide posts, would subject the "perfect blend" to competition from inferior merchandise.

We have already seen some of these influences in action. Fibers which fortuitously acquire glamor associations have been introduced in blends, in which they made no quality contribution, merely for their sales appeal. Fibers with peculiar plus characteristics when used alone have been incorporated on the assumption that their mere presence will lend to the blend all of their advantages with none of their disadvantages. Cheap fibers, which might be used in small quantities to give a reduced price with only minor reduction in quality, are added in ever increasing proportions to undersell the "safe" dilution.

Quite beyond the tendency of blend standards to shift under commercial pressures, there is the considerably more complex problem of predicting the performance of any blend. In appraising fabric performance of traditional fibers, we start out with a long history of actual service in the many fabric types which have been developed through the long and exhaustive procedure of trial and error. We are only beginning to develop a theory to anticipate fabric performance in a few simple structures of fabrics made from 100 per cent stocks of new fibers of known properties.

When blends are used, the interrelationships between fibers, as they perform their functions in the fabric structure, become extremely important. The simple mathematical assumptions based on proportions of fibers can be extremely misleading. When this very unpredictable interrelationship is superimposed upon a theory which is, itself, fragmentary at best, little can be assumed without exhaustive service tests. Furthermore, the way different fibers of differing properties behave in concert varies according to the influence of yarn and fabric construction. In addition the expected performance varies widely with the individual and his activities. Many performance demands do not lend themselves to laboratory representation or to scientific or engineering definition.

In view of the above, it is not difficult to understand that blends cannot be approached with any simple short-term development. Each combination of fibers, in actual proportions to be used, in specific fabric constructions made into garments of specific design must be tested under all of the tremendous variety of service exposures we are accustomed to provide.

Science and engineering techniques are gradually working out the background that may eventually give the industry adequate control of these vastly more complex structures. Until then, long performance experience is the only criterion for blend development, and the natural haste to offer the new and novel to stimulate sales must be held in check lest the entire principle of blending becomes discredited. When blends of tested and proved quality are established, means must be found to identify them so the consumer can recognize them as distinguished from untried or inferior approximations.

Summary

It can be seen from the discussion presented here that apparel fabrics are called upon to fulfill many critical requirements to give satisfaction. To meet these, it is necessary that the fibers in the fabric have the entire pattern of required properties.

We wear our garments under a wide variety of conditions and each garment must give satisfaction under all of the conditions associated with its type and style. It is quite possible to make special purpose fabrics with particular characteristics for limited uses, thus sacrificing versatility for excellence in a restricted field. Similarly, it is possible to demonstrate performance of a fabric in a single requirement, or a carefully selected group of requirements, while ignoring limitations in other directions. There is always a temptation to feature new properties and their special functions.

The cost of clothing represents an important section of the family budget. In this, the unit cost of each of the major items such as coats, suits and dresses, is too high to encourage experiment or search for novelty in their selection. At present, and for the next decade, there will be many new fabrics featured in advertising built around novel performance claims. In considering such claims the purchaser should ask,—

"How important is the particular type of claimed performance in my overall pattern of requirements?"

Wool has earned its enviable place in our wardrobes

because of its whole pattern of properties and their effectiveness in the whole range of service we require. These properties may be summed up as follows:

1. A wide choice in length, diameter and crimp characteristics which assist in providing a range of textures and constructions.
2. An extensibility which gives freedom of movement; distributes stresses; and provides unique characteristics of hand, drape and comfort.
3. A bulking power which gives uniform porous constructions coupled with good covering power; entraps large quantities of air to provide warmth at low weight; and permits fiber adjustment to avoid local damage. This characteristic also contributes to rain repellency by the absorption of energy from the falling droplets.
4. A resilience which contributes to a wool garment's fit and wrinkle resistance; maintains the insulation value of fabrics as they are worn; provides a hairy surface even when wet to assist in repelling rain, to entrap air to increase warmth, and to give a warm feeling to the touch. This characteristic is also responsible for many texture effects and discourages soiling.
5. A high absorbency which greatly assists in the maintenance of warmth, prevents chilling on changes in activity or exposure, and reduces static. This high absorbency is uniquely coupled with high resilience.
6. A stress-strain behavior which gives crispness without harshness and contributes much to the hand and drape of the woolen and worsted fabrics.
7. A complex chemical structure with many active chem-

ical groups which allows a wide choice in the selection of dyes to give desired balance of color values and permanence.

8. A unique felting power which provides the sole means of fiber assembly in a wide range of mechanical felts and is utilized in creating a wide variety of special fabric finishes.
9. A toughness and resistance to flex fatigue as well as high energy absorption which provide long wear.

Bibliography

American Association of Textile Chemists and Colorists Report and *Laundry Industry Report;* Am. Dyestuff Reptr., 39: 257, April 17, 1950.

ALEXANDER, P. AND CHARMAN, D. A., *Kinetics of Wool Dyeing. Part II: Adsorption of Surface-Active Dyes by Wool and Other Fibers;* Text. Research J., 20:761, 1950.

ASTBURY, W. T., Lecture on *How the Wool Molecule Works, and Its Further Significance in Biology and Medicine* at the Royal Society of Arts, London, November 15, 1951; published by the International Wool Secretariat, London, 1951.

BACKER, S., *Relationship Between the Structural Geometry of a Textile Fabric and Its Physical Properties. Part I: Literature Review;* Text. Research J., 18:650, 1948. *Part II: The Mechanics of Fabric Abrasion;* Text. Research J., 21:453. *Part IV: Interstice Geometry and Air Permeability;* Text. Research J., 21:703, 1951.

——— AND TANENHAUS, S. J., *Relationship Between the Structural Geometry of a Textile Fabric and Its Physical Properties. Part III: Textile Geometry and Abrasion-Resistance;* Text. Research J., 21:635, 1951.

BALL, H. J., *Problems Which Abrasion and Wear Testing Present;* Text. Research J., 8:134, 1938.

BARACH, J. L. AND RAINARD, L. W., *Effect of Crimp on Fiber Behavior. Part II: Addition of Crimp to Wool Fibers and Its Effect on Fiber Properties;* Text. Research J., 20:308, 1950.

BAXTER, S. AND CASSIE, A. B. D., *Water Repellency of Fabrics and a New Water Repellency Test;* J. Text. Inst., 36:T67, 1945.

BÖHRINGER, H., *Staple Fiber Research: Comparative Tests on Wool Type Staple Fibers;* Developments in the Wear Resistance of Textiles and Related Papers Published in Germany during World War II, Melliand Textilberichte, Heidelberg, 1949.

BOGATY, H., WEINER, L. I., SOOKNE, A. M., COZART, M. L. AND HARRIS, M., *Some Effects of Construction on the Laundering Shrinkage of Wool Fabrics;* Text. Research J., 21:895, 1951.

BOGATY, H., WEINER, L. I., SOOKNE, A. M. AND HARRIS, M., *Effect of Construction on the Laundering Shrinkage of Knitted Woolens;* Text. Research J., 21:102, 1951.

BREAZEALE, F., *Apparatus for Determining Coefficient of Friction of Running Yarn;* Text. Research J., 17:27, 1947.

BROWN, A. E., HORNSTEIN, L. R. AND HARRIS, M., *Chemical Modification of Wool—Treatment with Formaldehyde Solutions;* Text. Research J., 21:222, 1951.

———, PENDERGRASS, J. H. AND HARRIS, M., *Prevention of Supercontraction in Modified Wool Fibers* (Letters to the Editor); Text. Research J., 20:51, 1950.

BURGESS, R., *Protection of Wool Against Insects by Mitin FF and DDT;* Soc. Chem. Ind. J., 68:121, April 1949.

BURTE, H. M., *Effect of Dilute Salt Solutions on the Mechanical Properties of Animal Fibers* (Letters to the Editor); Text. Research J., 20:880, 1950.

———, *The Detection of Modification in Animal Fibers. I: Use of the Ratio* $\frac{(Hookean\ Slope\ in\ H_2O)}{(Hookean\ Slope\ in\ Conditioned\ Air)}$; Text. Research J., 21:63, 1951.

CARLENE, P. W., *Measurement of the Bending Modulus of Monofils;* J. Text. Inst., 38:T38, 1947.

CARTER, E. G., Lecture on *The Scientist Looks at Wool* at the Royal Society of Arts, London, February 8, 1951; published by the International Wool Secretariat, London, 1951.

CASSIE, A. B. D., *Physical Properties of Fibres and Textile Performances;* J. Text. Inst., 37:P154, 1946.

———, *Physics and Clothing;* Reports on Progress Physics, X:141, The Physical Society Great Britain, Physics of Clothes, Wool Industries Research Assoc., 1946.

———, *Characteristics for Warmth in Underwear Fabrics;* J. Text. Inst., 40:P444, 1949.

——— AND ROSE, L., *Natural Fibres* versus *Man-Made Fibres;* J. Text. Inst., 37:P556, 1946.

CHU, C. C., CUMMINGS, C. L. AND TEIXEIRA, N. A., *Mechanics of Elastic Performance of Textile Materials. Part V: A Study of the Factors Affecting the Drape of Fabrics—De-*

velopment of a Drape Meter; Text. Research J., 20:539, 1950.

COLLINS, G. E., *Construction of Fabrics for Specific Purposes;* J. Text. Inst., 37:P392, 1946.

CORRY, W. A., *Studies of Summer Weight Tropical Worsted Fabrics Made with Polyester Fibers and Blends of Polyester Fibers;* J. Text. Inst., 43:P670, 1952.

CRANSHAW, H., MORTON, W. E. AND BROWN, K. C., *Experiments on Fabric Wear Testing;* J. Text. Inst., 22:T64, 1931.

CROCKATT, A. J., *Cleanable Outerwear;* J. Text. Inst., 40:P1000, 1949.

DAVIES, E. J., *Reactions of Garment Fabrics, Accessories, and Methods of Garment Manufacture to Dry-Cleaning;* J. Text. Inst., 42:P820, 1951.

DUNELL, B. A. AND DILLON, J. H., *The Measurement of Dynamic Modulus and Energy Losses in Single Textile Filaments Subject to Forced Longitudinal Vibrations;* Text. Research J., 21:393, 1951.

DUNKERLEY, J. R., *Wear Resistance of Fibers;* Textile Industries, 112:110, December 1948.

FONG, W., YEISER, A. S. AND LUNDGREN, H. P., *A New Method for Raw-Wool Scouring and Grease Recovery;* Text. Research J., 21:540, 1951.

FOURT, L., SOOKNE, A. M., FRISHMAN, D. AND HARRIS, M., *The Rate of Drying of Fabrics;* Text. Research J., 21:26, 1951.

FULTON, G. P. AND JOHNSON, A. E., *Processes Used in Dry Cleaning Plants;* Papers of the Am. Assoc. Textile Technologists, 5:87, 1950.

GIBSON, W. H., *The Serviceability of Fabrics in Regard to Wear;* J. Text. Inst., 28:P212, 1937.

GOODINGS, A. C., *Molecular Structure of Wool Keratin;* Text. Research J., 20:454, 1950.

GRALÉN, N. AND OLOFSSON, B., *Measurement of Friction Between Single Fibers;* Text. Research J., 17:488, 1947.

HAMBURGER, W. J., *Mechanics of Elastic Performance of Textile Materials. I: Development of an Elastic Performance Coefficient in Tension;* Text. Research J., 18:102, 1948.

HARDY, J. I., *Wool Growth as Affected by Environment and Other Factors;* Text. Research J., 20:189, 1950.

Harris Research Laboratory, *Quartermaster Research on Water-Resistant Textiles;* Research and Development Report,

Textile Series Report No. 37, Department of the Army, Office of the Quartermaster General, 1951.

HERRINGTON, L. P., *Clothing from a Biophysical Point of View;* Papers of the Am. Assoc. Textile Technologists, 7:30, 1951.

HOFFMAN, R. M., *A Generalized Concept of Resilience;* Text. Research J., 18:141, 1948.

———, *Some Theoretical Aspects of Yarn and Fabric Density;* Text. Research J., 22:170, 1952.

——— AND BESTE, L. F., *Some Relations of Fiber Properties to Fabric Hand;* Text. Research J., 21:66, 1951.

HOPKINS, G. E., *Wool as an Apparel Fiber;* Text. Research J., 20:592, 1950.

HOTTE, G. H., *An Investigation of Fabric Structure and Its Relation to Certain Physical Properties;* Text. Research J., 20:811, 1950.

INGHAM, J. S., *Some Consumers' Observations on Fabrics and Garments Made from Blended Yarns;* J. Text. Inst., 43: P612, 1952.

JOHNSTON, L. G., *Consumer Complaints from New Fabrics and Finishes;* Am. Dyestuff Reptr., 38:65, January 24, 1949.

JONES, H. W. AND LUNDGREN, H. P., *Modification of Wool with* Beta-*Propiolactone. Part I: The Chemistry of the Reaction;* Text. Research J., 21:620. *Part II: Effect on Rate and Degree of Felting;* Text. Research J., 21:629, 1951.

KÄRRHOLM, M. AND KÄRRHOLM, G., *Impact of Raindrops on Fabrics;* Text. Research J., 20:215, 1950.

KÄRRHOLM, E. M., *Testing of Water-Repellency;* J. Text. Inst., 43:P263, 1952.

KASWELL, E. R., *Textile Fibers, Yarns and Fabrics. A Comparative Survey of Their Behavior with Special Reference to Wool;* Reinhold Publishing Corp., New York, 1953.

———, *Wear-Resistance of Apparel Textiles. I: Tests of Military Fabrics on Quartermaster Combat Course;* Text. Research J., 16:413, 1946.

——— AND PLATT, M. M., *Mechanics of Elastic Performance of Textile Materials. Part VII: Mechanical Properties of Hard Fibers with Reference to Their Use in Cordage Structures;* Text. Research J., 21:263, 1951.

KATZ, S. M. AND TOBOLSKY, A. V., *Relaxation of Stress in Wool Fibers;* Text. Research J., 20:87, 1950.

KENNEDY, S. J., *Importance of Conservation to the Textile Industry and the American Public;* Papers of the Am. Assoc. Textile Technologists, 6:65, 1951.

———, *Fiber Blends in Military Textiles;* J. Text. Inst., 43: P681, 1952.

KING, G. AND WARBURTON, F. L., *Saturation Moisture Absorption of Wool* (Letters to the Editor); J. Text. Inst., 43: T516, 1952.

LAGERMALM, G. AND PHILIP, B., *Action of Alkali on the Epicuticle of Wool;* Text. Research J., 20:668, 1950.

LEADERMAN, H., *Elastic and Creep Properties of Filamentous Materials and Other High Polymers;* Textile Foundation, Washington, 1943.

LECOMPTE, G. AND LIPP, H. H., *Investigation of Methods of Testing for Moisture in Wool;* Am. Dyestuff Reptr., 38: 484, June 27, 1949.

LEMON, H., Lecture on *Science in the Service of Wool* at the Royal Society of Arts, London, March 26, 1952; published by the International Wool Secretariat, London, 1952.

LINCOLN, B., *Flexural Fatigue and Visco-Elastic Properties of Wool Fibres;* J. Text. Inst., 43:T158, 1952.

LINDBERG, J., *Measurement of Friction Between Single Fibers. III: Influence of Different Treatments on the Frictional Properties of Wool Fibers;* Text. Research J., 18:470, 1948.

———, *Rate of Acid Sorption by Wool Fibers;* Text. Research J., 20:381, 1950.

LIPSON, M. AND HOWARD, P., *Friction Between Keratin Surfaces as Affected by Some Shrinkproofing Treatments;* J. Soc. Dyers & Col., 62:29, 1946.

LITTLE, R. W., *Fundamentals of Flame Retardancy;* Text. Research J., 21:901, 1951.

LOMAX, J., *Serviceability of Fabrics in Regard to Wear. Testing Fabrics to Foretell Serviceability;* J. Text. Inst., 28:P218, 1937.

MAGINNIS, J. B., *Effect of Moisture on Twisted Yarns;* Text. Research J., 20:165, 1950.

MAHAL, G. S., JOHNSTON, A. AND BURNS, R. H., *Types and*

Dimensions of Fiber Scales from the Wool Types of Domestic Sheep and Wild Life; Text. Research J., 21:83, 1951.

MAKINSON, K. R., *Some Replica Techniques Useful in Electron Microscopy of the Surface of the Wool Fiber;* Text. Research J., 20:22, 1950.

MANN, J. C., *Testing of Fabrics for Resistance to Abrasion;* J. Text. Inst., 28:P220, 1937.

MARTIN, A. J. P., *Observations on the Theory of Felting;* J. Soc. Dyers & Col., 60:325, 1944.

MERCER, E. H. AND MAKINSON, K. R., *Frictional Properties of Wool and Other Textile Fibres;* J. Text. Inst., 38:T227, 1947.

MERSEREAU, E. P. AND RAINARD, L. W., *Color Changes in Wool During Processing;* Text. Research J., 21:239, 1951.

MILLSON, H. E. AND TURL, L. H., *Microscopial Dyeing Phenomena. Studies with the Microdyeoscope;* Text. Research J., 21:685, 1951.

NEWBURGH, L. H., *Physiology of Heat Regulation and the Science of Clothing;* W. B. Saunders Co., Philadelphia, 1949.

NUESSLE, A. C., *Abrasion-Resistance of Resin-Treated Fabrics* (Letters to the Editor); Text. Research J., 21:747, 1951.

O'REILLY, D. F., WHITWELL, J. C., STEELE, R. O. AND WAKELIN, J. H., *Properties of Apparel Wools. II: Modification of Fiber Surface During Worsted Processing;* Text. Research J., 22:441, 1952.

PAINTER, E. V., *Mechanics of Elastic Performance of Textile Materials. Part VIII: Graphical Analysis of Fabric Geometry;* Text. Research J., 22:153, 1952.

———, CHU, C. C. AND MORGAN, H. M., *Testing Textiles on the Elmendorf Tear Tester;* Text. Research J., 20:410, 1950.

PEIRCE, F. T., *The Geometry of Cloth Structure;* J. Text. Inst., 28:T45, 1937.

PENNER, S. E. AND ROBERTSON, A. F., *Flow Through Fabric-like Structures;* Text. Research J., 21:775, 1951.

PICKEN, J., *The Effect of Variation of Air Density and Temperature on the Airflow Characteristics of Porous Fabrics,* CP. No. 25, 12649, A.R.C. Technical Report; His Majesty's Stationery Office, London, 1950.

PLATT, M. M., *Mechanics of Elastic Performance of Textile*

Materials. Part III: Some Aspects of Stress Analysis of Textile Structures—Continuous-Filament Yarns; Text. Research J., 20:1. *Part IV: Some Aspects of Stress Analysis of Textile Structures—Staple-Fiber Yarns;* Text. Research J., 20:519. *Part VI: Influence of Yarn Twist on Modulus of Elasticity;* Text. Research J., 20:665, 1950.

PRESTON, J. M. AND NIMKAR, M. V., *Capillary Phenomena in Assemblies of Fibres;* J. Text. Inst., 43:T402, 1952.

RAINARD, L. W. AND ABBOTT, D., *Effect of Crimp on Fiber Behavior. Part I: Determination of Fiber Irregularities and the Concepts of the Single-Fiber Bulking Capacity;* Text. Research J., 20:301, 1950.

REES, W. H., *The Over-All Specific Volume, Compressibility and Resilience of Fibrous Materials;* J. Text. Inst., 39: T131, 1948.

———, "*Wool as an Apparel Fiber,*" *by Hopkins* (Letters to the Editor); Text. Research J., 20:881, 1950.

RIPA, O. AND SPEAKMAN, J. B., *The Plasticity of Wool;* Text. Research J., 21:215, 1951.

ROBERTSON, A. F., *Air Porosity of Open-Weave Fabrics. Part I: Metallic Meshes;* Text. Research J., 20:838. *Part II: Textile Fabrics;* Text. Research J., 20:844, 1950.

SCHIEFER, H. F., STEVENS, H. T., MACH, P. B. AND BOYLAND, P. M., *A Study of the Properties of Household Blankets;* J. Research Natl. Bur. Standards, 32:261, 1944.

SCHWARZ, E. R., *Twist Structure of Plied Yarns;* Text. Research J., 20:175, 1950.

———, *Predicting Textile Performance;* Papers of the Am. Assoc. Textile Technologists, 6:149, 1951.

SIU, R. G. H., *Mechanism of Microbiological Decomposition of Cellulose;* Text. Research J., 20:281, 1950.

——— AND MANDELS, G. R., *Rapid Method for Determining Mildew Susceptibility of Materials and Disinfecting Activity of Compounds;* Text. Research J., 20:516, 1950.

SMITH, H. DEWITT, *Textile Fibers. An Engineering Approach to Their Properties and Utilization;* Edgar Marburg Lecture, American Society for Testing Materials, 47th Annual Meeting, 1944.

SOOKNE, A. M., BOGATY, H. AND HARRIS, M., *Some Felting Properties of Wools of Different Geographical Origins;* Text. Research J., 20:637, 1950.

SPEAKMAN, J. B. AND COOPER, C. A., *Adsorption of Water by Wool. III: Influence of Temperature on the Affinity of Wool for Water;* J. Text. Inst., 27:T191, 1936.

STAHL, W. H., MCQUE, B., MANDELS, G. R. AND SIU, R. G. H., *Studies on the Microbiological Degradation of Wool. Digestion of Normal and Modified Fibrillar Proteins;* Text. Research J., 20:570, 1950.

STOLL, R. G., *Engineering of Wear Resistant Fabrics;* Papers of the Am. Assoc. Textile Technologists, 6:71, 1951.

———, *Functional Characteristics of Wool Fabrics for Military Uses;* Papers of the Am. Assoc. Textile Technologists, 6:80, 1951.

SUSICH, G. AND BACKER, S., *Tensile Recovery Behavior of Textile Fibers;* Text. Research J., 21:482, 1951.

TALLANT, J. D. AND WORNER, R. K., *Apparatus for Evaluating Warmth of Textile Fabrics;* Text. Research J., 21:591, 1951.

Textile World, Synthetic-Fiber Chart; McGraw-Hill Publishing Co., New York, 1951.

THOMSON, R. H. K. AND TRAILL, D., *Bending Fracture of Fibres;* J. Text. Inst., 38:T43, 1947.

TOBOLSKY, A. V., DUNELL, B. A. AND ANDREWS, R. D., *Stress Relaxation and Dynamic Properties of Polymers;* Text. Research J., 21:404, 1951.

VAN WYK, C. M., *Note on the Compressibility of Wool;* J. Text. Inst., 37:T285, 1946.

VON BERGEN, W. AND CLUTZ, C. S., *Dimensional Stability of Woolen and Worsted Fabrics;* Text. Research J., 20:580, 1950.

——— AND MAUERSBERGER, H. R., *American Wool Handbook,* 2nd Edition; Textile Book Publishers, Inc., New York, 1948.

——— AND WAKELIN, J. H., *Properties of Apparel Wools. I: Preliminary Report on Worsted Processing Trials;* Text. Research J., 22:123, 1952.

WAGNER, E., *Influence of Different Finishes on the Serviceability of Staple Rayon Shirting;* Developments in the Wear Resistance of Textiles and Related Papers Published in Germany during World War II, Melliand Textilberichte, Heidelberg, 1949.

WARD, W. H., *The Molecular Size of Proteins from Several*

Wools Solubilized in Aqueous Urea; Text. Research J., 22:405, 1952.

WEINER, L. I., *Some Principles of Construction of Water Resistant Fabrics;* Papers of the Am. Assoc. Textile Technologists, 6:85, 1951.

WINSLOW, C. E. A. AND HERRINGTON, L. P., *Temperature and Human Life;* Princeton University Press, Princeton, 1949.

Index

ABOUT THE AUTHOR

Giles E. Hopkins, a native of Massachusetts, is a graduate of the Massachusetts Institute of Technology with a degree in chemical engineering. In the course of twelve years' service as technical director of the Bigelow-Sanford Carpet Company, he pioneered the organization of functionalized research and development in textile mills. Throughout his career he has been active in leading the cooperative attack on research problems in and out of the textile industry, initiating the wool subcommittee of the American Society for Testing Materials of which he became a director. He has taken an active part in the Fiber Society, the American Association of Textile Chemists and Colorists and the American Association for Textile Technology. He was director of applied research at the Textile Research Institute and consultant to the National Cotton Council.

Mr. Hopkins was a member of a steering committee appointed by the National Research Council to study industrial research administration problems. This study resulted in the organization of the Industrial Research Institute of which he was an executive committee member. He was also a charter member and director of the New York Association of Research Directors and lectured on research administration at the Graduate School of New York University and the Polytechnic Institute of Brooklyn.

Mr. Hopkins has been technical director of The Wool Bureau, Inc., since its inception in 1949 where he maintains contact with wool research throughout the world. He is the author of numerous articles on wool and its performance.